CATALYST 2G

A framework for success

Carol Chapman
Moira Sheehan

Heinemann
Inspiring generations

Contents

Introduction iv
Key ideas viii

A Food and digestion

A1 What's in food? 2
A2 Balanced diet 4
A3 Healthy or not? 6
A4 Total breakdown 8
A5 Taking it in 10
T **A6** Chewing it over 12

B Respiration

B1 Food for energy 14
B2 Everything respires 16
B3 Breathe in and out 18
B4 A transport system 20
T **B5** Trouble with yeast 22

C Microbes and disease

C1 Going on growing 24
C2 Defence systems 26
C3 Killing bacteria 28
C4 Fighting infection 30
C5 The battle goes on 32
T **C6** Testing medicines 34

D Ecological relationships

D1 Plant groups 36
D2 A place to live 38
D3 Home alone? 40
D4 Populations 42
T **D5** Special daisies 44

E Atoms and elements

E1 It's elementary 46
E2 The elements 48
E3 How elements differ 50
T **E4** Getting it right 52
E5 Reacting elements 54

F Compounds and mixtures

F1 Compounds all around 56
F2 Reacting compounds 58
F3 What's in it? 60
F4 The air around us 62
T **F5** Formulae 64

G Rocks and weathering

G1 Rock breaking 66

G2 Disappearing rocks 68

G3 Transporting rock 70

G4 Layers of sediment 72

T **G5** Earth detectives 74

H The rock cycle

H1 Hard rock 76

H2 Cool rocks? 78

H3 Rock on 80

T **H4** Name that rock 82

I Heating and cooling

I1 What temperature? 84

I2 Temperature and energy 86

I3 Bigger and smaller 88

I4 All change 90

I5 Conduction 92

I6 Convection 94

I7 Evaporation, radiation 96

T **I8** Explaining the results 98

J Magnets and electromagnets

J1 Magnetic fields 100

J2 Magnets 102

J3 Making magnets 104

J4 Electromagnets 106

T **J5** Variables 108

K Light

K1 Seeing the light 110

K2 Which ray? 112

K3 Travelling through? 114

K4 Coloured light 116

T **K5** Mix it 118

L Sound and hearing

L1 Good vibrations 120

L2 Passing through 122

L3 Hearing the sound 124

L4 Turn it down! 126

T **L5** Detect it 128

Glossary 130

Index 140

T indicates Think about spread

iii

Introduction

Welcome to Catalyst

This is the second of three books designed to help you learn all the science ideas you need during Key Stage 3. We hope you'll enjoy the books as well as learning a lot from them.

The first four pages of the book look back at what you learnt about energy, cells, particles, forces and interdependence in year 7. These are called Key ideas and the pages will help you to remember some important facts about them. You will learn more about these ideas as you go through the book.

This book has twelve units which each cover a different topic.
The units have two types of pages:

Learn about:

Most of the double-page spreads in a unit introduce and explain new ideas about the topic. They start with a list of these so that you can see what you are going to learn about.

Think about:

Each unit has a double-page spread called Think about. You will work in pairs or small groups and discuss your answers to the questions. These pages will help you understand how scientists work and how ideas about science develop.

On the pages there are these symbols:

a   Quick questions scattered through the pages help you check your knowledge and understanding of the ideas as you go along, for example,

    a **Use the particle model to explain why the liquid will not squash.**

Questions

The questions at the end of the spread help you check you understand all the important ideas.

For your notes:

These list the important ideas from the spread to help you learn, write notes and revise.

Do you remember?

These remind you of what you already know about the topic.

Did you know?

These tell you interesting or unusual things, such as the history of some science inventions and ideas.

At the back of the book:

Glossary

All the important scientific words in the text appear in bold type. They are listed with their meanings in the Glossary at the back of the book. Look there to remind yourself what they mean.

Index

There is an Index at the very back of the book, where you can find out which pages cover a particular topic.

Activities to help or check your learning:

Your teacher may give you these activities from the teacher's materials which go with the course:

Unit map

You can use this to think about what you already know about a topic. You can also use it to revise a topic before a test or exam.

Starters

When you start a lesson this is a short activity to introduce what you are going to learn about.

Activity

There are different types of activities, including investigations, that your teacher can give you to help with the topics in each spread in the pupil book.

Plenaries

At the end of a lesson your teacher may give you a short activity to summarise what you have learnt.

Homework

At the end of a lesson the teacher may give you one of the homework sheets that go with the lesson. This will help you to review and revise what you learnt in the lesson.

Pupil checklist

This is a checklist of what you should have learnt to help you with your revision.

Test yourself

You can use this quiz at the end of each unit to see what you are good at and what you might need to revise.

End of unit test Green

This helps you and your teacher check what you learnt during the unit, and measures your progress and success.

Heinemann Educational Publishers
Halley Court, Jordan Hill, Oxford OX2 8EJ
Part of Harcourt Education

Heinemann is the registered trademark of
Harcourt Education Limited

© Carol Chapman, Moira Sheehan 2003

First published 2003

07 06 05 04
10 9 8 7 6 5 4 3

British Library Cataloguing in Publication Data is available
from the British Library on request.

ISBN 0 435 76031 9

Edited by Diona Gregory, Ruth Holmes and Sarah Ware
Designed and typeset by Ken Vail Graphic Design

Original illustrations © Harcourt Education Limited 2003

Illustrated by Jeff Edwards, Stuart Harrison, David Lock, Richard Morris, John Plumb,
Sylvie Poggio Artists Agency (Rhiannon Powell and Lisa Smith), Simon Girling & Associates
(Mike Lacey)

Printed in the UK by Scotprint.

Picture research by Jennifer Johnson

Acknowledgements
The authors and publishers would like to thank the following for permission to use
copyright material: **5 a day leaflet p5** Reproduced with permission of the Department of
Health and the Controller of Her Majesty's Stationary Office, © Crown copyright.

The publishers have made every effort to trace the copyright holders, but if they have
inadvertently overlooked any, they will be pleased to make the necessary
arrangements at the first opportunity.

p75 The concept of 'lateral thinking' was originated by Edward de Bono.

For photograph acknowledgements, please see page vii.

Tel: 01865 888058 www.heinemann.co.uk

The author and publishers would like to thank the following for permission to use photographs:

T = top   **B** = bottom   **L** = left   **R** = right   **M** = middle

SPL = Science Photo Library

Cover: Getty Images.

Page 2, **T**: Photofusion; 2, **M**, **B** x3: Andrew Lambert; 4, x2: Corbis; 9: Wellcome Trust, courtesy of Charles C Thomas Publishers; 11, **T**: SPL/Eye of Science; 11, **B**: SPL; 14: Empics; 15: Photodisc; 16: Corbis; 21: Wellcome Trust; 24: Corbis; 25, x2: Pete Morris; 26, **L**: SPL/CNRI; 26, **M**: SPL/HC Robinson; 26, **R**: SPL/Dr P Marazzi; 28, **T**: Pete Morris; 28, **M**: Philip Parkhouse; 28, **B**: Mary Evans Picture Library; 29, **T**: SmithKlein Beecham; 29, **B**: Pete Morris; 30, **L**: BAL; 30, **R**: Wellcome Trust; 32: John Beck; 33: Panos Pictures; 34: SPL/TEK Image; 36, **T**: NHPA/James Carmichael Jr; 36, **ML**: Wildlife Matters; 36, **MR**: Garden Matters/Steffie Shields; 36, **BL**: SPL/John Howard; 36, **BR**: SPL/Alex Bartel; 37, **TL**: SPL/Simon Fraser; 37, **TR**: SPL/Claude Nuridsany & Marie Perennou; 37, **BL**: SPL/Eye of Science; 37, **BR**: SPL/Simon Fraser; 38, **T**: Garden & Wildlife Matters; 38, **B** x2: Peter Gould; 39, **T**: Oxford Scientific Films/Colin Milkins; 39, **B**: Robert Harding/Adam Woolfitt; 40: Oxford Scientific Films/GI Bernard; 45, x2: Andrew Lambert; 46, **T**: Andrew Lambert; 46, **BL**: Peter Gould; 46, **BR**: Corbis; 47, **L**: Panos; 47, **R**: SPL/Bernhard Edmaier; 49: Mary Evans Picture Library; 50, **T**, **BR**: Gareth Boden; 50, **BL** x3: Peter Gould; 51: Gareth Boden; 54, x4: Gareth Boden; 56, **L**: SPL/Victor de Schwanberg; 56, **R**: Peter Gould; 57, x2: Peter Gould; 58, x2: Peter Gould; 59: Peter Gould; 60, **T**: Pete Morris; 61, **L**: Alvey & Towers; 61, **R**: Moira Sheehan; 63, **L**: SPL; 63, **R**: SPL/Jerome Yeats; 66, x4: GSF Picture Library; 67, GSF Picture Library; 68, **TL**: Andrew Lambert; 68, **TR**: GSF Picture Library; 68, **B**: Environmental Images/John Morrison; 69: Robert Harding/Roy Rainford; 70, **T**, **BL**: GSF Picture Library; 70, **BR**: Corbis; 71: Environmental Images/Clive Jones; 73: Corbis; 74, x3: The Natural History Museum; 77, **TL**, **TR**, **BL**: GSF Picture Library; 77, **M**, **BR**: Corbis; 78, x3: GSF Picture Library; 81, **T**, **M3**, **B**: GSF Picture Library; 81, **M1**, **M2**: Corbis; 83, **L**, **R**: Corbis; 83, **M**: GSF Picture Library; 84, **TL**: SPL/Chris Priest & Mark Clarke; 84, **TR**, **BL**: Peter Gould; 84, **BR**: Pete Morris; 87, **L**: Corbis; 87, **R**: SPL/James Holmes; 88, **T**: Milepost 92$^1/_2$; 88, **B**: Corbis; 89: Peter Gould; 93: Corbis; 94, x2: Peter Gould; 96, **TL**: PhotoObjects, 96, **TR**: Empics; 96, **B**: SPL; 98: Peter Gould; 100, **T**: Bea Thomas; 100, **M**: Richard Thomas; 100, **B** x2: Peter Gould; 101: Gareth Boden; 102, **T**: National Maritime Museum; 102, **B**: ActionPlus; 103: Peter Gould; 104, x3: Peter Gould; 105, x2: Peter Gould; 106, **T**: Alamy; 106, **ML**, **B**: Gareth Boden; 106, **MR**: Peter Gould; 107: Milepost 92$^1/_2$; 110, **T**: Corbis; 110, **B**: Andrew Lambert; 111, **TL**: SPL/Adam Hart-Davis; 111, **TM**: Alvey and Towers; 111, **TR**: Pete Morris; 111, **B**: SPL/Space Telescope Science Institute/NASA; 112, **TL**: Corbis; 112, **TR**: SPL/David Nunuk; 112, **B**: SPL/David Scharf; 113, **L**: Trevor Hill; 113, **R**: Bea Thomas; 114, x2: Andrew Lambert; 115: Andrew Lambert; 116, **TL**, **B**: Corbis; 116, **TR**: SPL/David Parker; 118: SPL/Vaughan Fleming; 120, **T**: Trevor Clifford; 120, **B**: Peter Gould; 123: SPL/Pat & Tom Leeson; 124: SPL/Quest; 125: Bea Thomas; 126, **L**: Redferns; 126, **R**: Holt Studios; 128: SPL; 129, **T**: Gareth Boden; 129, **B**: SPL/Tek Image.

Key ideas

Learn about:
- Energy
- Cells
- Particles
- Forces
- Interdependence

Energy, cells, particles, forces and interdependence are five key scientific ideas.

Energy is probably the most important idea in science.

Energy

Energy makes things happen.

Energy can be **transferred**.

Light energy, sound energy, heat energy and *electrical energy* are all energy on the move.

Energy can be stored.

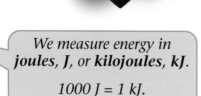

*We measure energy in joules, **J**, or **kilojoules, kJ**.*

1000 J = 1 kJ.

Energy stored as
strain energy.

Energy stored as
chemical energy.

Energy stored as
gravitational energy.

viii

Cells

All living things are made of **cells**.

Cells contain a **nucleus**, **cytoplasm** and a **cell membrane**.

Plant cells also have a **cell wall**. Some plant cells have a large **vacuole**. Plant cells from leaves also have **chloroplasts**.

The nucleus contains the instructions to make the cell work.

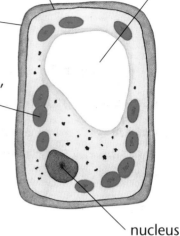

The vacuole is full of liquid.

cell membrane

The cell wall is like a box.

The chloroplasts contain **chlorophyll**, a green pigment.

The cell membrane lets some things in and out of the cell.

The cytoplasm is where chemical reactions take place.

nucleus

Cells work together in a **tissue** and tissues are grouped together to make **organs**.

The heart is an example of an organ. It contains muscle tissue, nervous tissue and blood vessels.

Particles

All materials are made up of **particles**.

Scientists use the particle model to explain solids, liquids and gases.

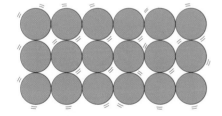

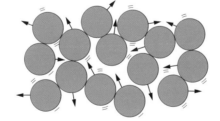

In solids the particles:

- are in rows
- are touching
- vibrate on the spot
- are held together.

In liquids the particles:

- are disordered
- are touching
- vibrate and slide over each other
- are held together.

In gases the particles:

- are disordered
- are far apart
- zoom about
- are not held together.

This **particle model** can explain melting, freezing, boiling and condensing.

It can also explain dissolving, expanding and diffusion.

Key ideas (continued)

Forces

Forces are pulls, pushes and twists. Forces have size and direction.

Balanced forces

We show forces with arrows. The length shows the size of the force. The arrowhead shows the direction of the force.

The boy does not move because the forces are equal but opposite.

Unbalanced forces

The boy moves to the right.

The boy moves to the left.

Weight is the force we feel because of gravity. Other forces include **friction**, **upthrust** and **air resistance**.

*We measure forces in **newtons**, N.*

Interdependence

Each organism relies on other organisms to stay alive.

The green hairstreak butterfly

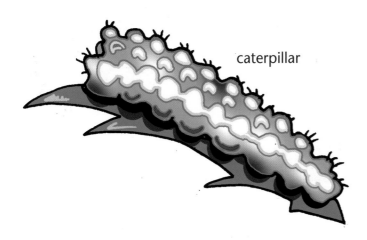

caterpillar

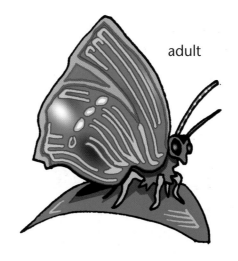

adult

Birds eat the green hairstreak caterpillars and butterflies.

It pollinates plants when it goes from flower to flower collecting nectar.

It needs plants like bilberry, gorse and heather for:

- food as a caterpillar (leaves)
- food as an adult (nectar)
- camouflage
- shelter
- a place to lay its eggs.

If they had no predators, the green hairstreak caterpillars would eat all the leaves and the plants would die. Then the caterpillars and butterflies would starve.

Food chains and **food webs** show what organisms eat.

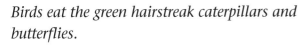

bilberry → green hairstreak → bird

- The **producer** always comes first.
  It makes its own food using sunlight.
- **Consumers** eat other organisms.
- The arrows show the flow of energy.

A food web is many food chains put together.

The green hairstreak needs the plants, and the plants need the green hairstreak.

A1 What's in food?

Food for thought ...

All animals and plants need food. Food gives us the energy we need to carry out our life processes. Plants use sunlight to make their own food from air and water. Animals have to find their food.

In this country many of us find our food in supermarkets. But how exactly do baked beans on toast or apples help to keep us alive, active and healthy?

What are nutrients?

Food contains many different substances. The useful ones are called **nutrients**. The main nutrients are **carbohydrates**, **fats** and **proteins**. They make up most of the food we eat.

NUTRITION		
TYPICAL COMPOSITION	A 30g serving with 125ml semi-skimmed milk provides	100g (3½oz) provide
Energy	718kJ/170kcal*	1560kJ/367kcal
Protein	6.3 g	7.3 g
Carbohydrate	31.1 g	82.7 g
of which sugars	8.9 g	8.9 g
Fat	2.2 g*	0.8 g
of which saturates	1.5 g	0.3 g
Fibre**	1.1 g	3.6 g
Sodium	0.4 g	1.1 g

VITAMINS/MINERALS

Vitamin D	1.6µg (32% RDA)	5.0µg (100% RDA)
Thiamin	0.5mg (34% RDA)	1.4mg (100% RDA)
Riboflavin	0.7mg (44% RDA)	1.6mg (100% RDA)
Niacin	6.5mg (36% RDA)	18.0mg (100% RDA)
Vitamin B6	0.7mg (34% RDA)	2.0mg (100% RDA)
Folic acid	127.5µg (63% RDA)	400.0µg (200% RDA)
Vitamin B12	0.8µg (80% RDA)	1.0µg (100% RDA)
Pantothenic acid	2.2mg (37% RDA)	6.0mg (100% RDA)
Iron	4.3mg (30% RDA)	14.0mg (100% RDA)

RDA = Recommended Daily Allowance

This pack contains approx 16 servings

INFORMATION

*Calories/Fat per serving with whole milk: 195 cals/5g

ⓐ Look at this food label. Find the main nutrients. How much of each one does this food contain?

Carbohydrates give you energy. They are found in bread, potatoes, cakes and sweets. Sugar and starch are both carbohydrates.

Proteins help your body to grow and repair itself. They are found in meat, fish, eggs, peas, beans and milk.

Fats also give you energy. You have a layer of fat under your skin that keeps you warm. Fats are found in butter, margarine, full-fat milk and meat.

ⓑ Name two foods that contain a lot of carbohydrates.

ⓒ Name two foods that contain a lot of fats.

ⓓ What does your body use proteins for?

Small amounts – vitamins and minerals

Vitamins are also needed in very small amounts to keep the body healthy. Different vitamins have different jobs. If a vitamin is missing from someone's diet, it can cause a disease.

Vitamin C is found in fruit and green vegetables. A lack of vitamin C causes the disease **scurvy**. The gums bleed, cuts don't heal and your teeth fall out.

e Long ago sailors who were at sea for months without fresh food suffered badly from scurvy. Then they started taking barrels of fresh fruit such as limes to eat. Scurvy was no longer a problem. Why?

Your body also needs **minerals** in small amounts. Different minerals have different jobs.

Calcium is found in milk and cheese. You need calcium for healthy teeth and bones.

f Why is milk good for your teeth and bones?

Fibre and water

Fibre is also needed in your diet. Fibre is sometimes called **roughage** and it is found in cereals, fruit and vegetables. It helps food to keep moving through your system. Fibre prevents you getting **constipated**.

Water from food and drink is also essential in your diet. You would die in a few days without water. All the chemical reactions in your body take place in water.

Did you know?

Your body loses about two litres of water a day, most of it as urine.

Questions

1 Match each nutrient with the use (**function**) it has in the body.

Nutrients	Functions
fat	needed for growth and repair
carbohydrate	needed in very small amounts to keep the body healthy
protein	provides energy and helps prevent the body losing heat
vitamins	provides energy

2 a Why is fibre good for you? **b** Which foods are high in fibre?

3 Write a rhyme to help you remember the major groups of nutrients. For example, Very Fit People Munch Carrots could stand for Vitamins Fats Proteins Minerals Carbohydrates.

For your notes:

- Food contains useful substances called **nutrients**.

- The most important types of nutrient are **carbohydrates**, **fats**, **proteins**, **vitamins** and **minerals**.

- **Fibre** and **water** are also needed for a healthy diet.

Getting the balance right

Your body needs all the nutrients, fibre and water to keep you fit and healthy. A diet that has the right amounts of all these is called a **balanced diet**.

Balanced diets can vary a lot. The balance is different for different people. The foods which make it up can be very different.

How much should we eat?

The amount of energy you need in your food depends on how much energy your body uses up every day. This depends on whether you are growing, how active you are and the size of your body. Men often need more energy than women.

Do you remember?

Food is the energy source for animals. We measure the energy value of food in kilojoules (kJ).

A teenage boy uses about 12 200 kJ of energy every day, while a girl of the same age, but with a smaller body mass, uses about 9600 kJ. A person doing a very active job such as a builder uses a lot more energy than an office worker of the same age and sex. A pregnant woman needs more energy than usual.

a Why do different people need different amounts of energy?

Balancing the energy

It is important to take in the right amount of energy in your food. Some people take in more energy than they use up. They risk becoming fat. People who are very overweight for their height are called **obese**.

Some people do not eat enough food to give them energy for their body's needs and they lose weight. Sometimes people can suffer from eating disorders such as **anorexia nervosa**. They eat hardly anything and they become very underweight. This disease can kill.

ⓑ **Explain why people get very fat or very thin.**

Different diets

People from different cultures eat different foods. This may be due to religion, tradition or simply what is available in the country.

In many Asian countries such as China, India and Pakistan the main carbohydrate is rice. In Europe, potatoes, bread or pasta are the main carbohydrate foods.

ⓒ **Write down the carbohydrate foods in your diet. (Don't forget the sweets and biscuits!)**

In developed countries such as the UK, people's diets often contain too much fat and salt. A person who eats a high-fat diet is more likely to have a heart attack. A diet high in salt can increase the risk of having strokes. This kind of diet is often called the 'Western diet'.

We also eat too little fresh fruit and vegetables. Government scientists encourage us to eat five portions of fruit or vegetables a day to keep healthy.

1 medium apple   1 cereal bowl of mixed salad   2 halves of canned peaches

1 handful of grapes   1 medium banana   3 heaped tablespoons of peas

1 medium glass of orange juice   7 strawberries   3 whole dried apricots

5 A DAY

Just Eat More (fruit & veg)   3 heaped tablespoons of cooked kidney beans   16 okra   NHS

Did you know?

Almost twenty per cent of the population of the UK are officially considered to be obese.

ⓓ **Write down all the fruit and vegetables you ate yesterday. Did you get your five portions?**

Questions

1 Copy and complete these sentences about balanced diets.

  a Your body needs nutrients for energy and …

  b A balanced diet gives you the right amounts of …

  c The amount of energy you need depends on …

2 Explain why a woman working in an office needs less energy than a man working on a building site.

3 In many developing countries people are now eating a more 'Western style' diet. What effect do you think this might have on their health?

For your notes:

● A diet that has the right amount of each nutrient is called a **balanced diet**.

● It is important to balance the energy in your food with the energy your body uses.

Healthy or not?

Breakfast on the move

Have you ever missed breakfast and had a cereal bar on the way to school instead? Cereal bars are advertised as the modern alternative to breakfast. They contain lots of nutrients including vitamins and fibre. They are easy to eat on the move – particularly useful if you are running late!

But some experts on healthy eating are worried that cereal bars are loaded with salt, sugar and fats.

a Why are cereal bars a popular alternative to breakfast?

A salty taste?

Some scientists think that too much salt in the diet can cause high blood pressure. This can increase the risk of heart disease and strokes. People in the UK eat 9 g of salt a day on average. Some scientists say we should cut this to 6 g.

A sweet tooth?

When we eat sugary food, microorganisms on our teeth feed on the sugar. This produces the acid that causes tooth decay.

Too much fat?

Eating too much fat, especially animal fats, can cause a layer of fat to build up in your blood vessels. This increases the risk of heart disease. Some scientists recommend that we eat very little of foods which have more than 14 g of fat out of every 100 g.

Did you know?

Eighty per cent of the salt we eat is added to food during processing.

Did you know?

The sugar in a cereal bar is more likely to stick to your teeth and cause tooth decay than the sugar in a bowl of breakfast cereal with milk. The milk washes the sugar away from your teeth!

NUTRITIONAL INFORMATION

100 g provides:
Energy 1900 kJ/450 kcal.
Protein 9 g.
Carbohydrates 67 g (of which sugars 37 g, starch 30 g).
Fat 16 g (of which saturates 14 g).
Fibre 1.6 g.
Salt 1.6 g.
Vitamins: Thiamine (B$_1$) 0.9 mg (65%). Riboflavin (B$_2$) 1.0 mg (65%). Niacin 11.3 mg (65%). Vitamin B$_6$ 1.3 mg (65%). Folic acid 125 μg (65%).
Minerals: Calcium 720 mg (90%). Iron 8.8 mg (65%).
(%) = % Recommended Daily Allowance.

One Cerius bar weighs 25 g.

b Look at the Cerius Bar label at the bottom of page 6.

  (i) How much fat does it have per 100 g?

  (ii) Is this more or less than the amount of fat scientists recommend?

  (iii) How many grams of salt does one bar contain? (*Hint:* the amounts in the label are for 100 g and one bar weighs 25 g.)

c Do you think a Cerius Bar is a healthy or unhealthy breakfast? Use the ingredients to justify your argument.

Time for lunch ...

Jordan decided to have baked beans on toast.

But baked beans, like most processed foods, have added sugar and salt. The salt is added to give flavour and improve the shelf life.

Bread also has added salt. Four slices of bread contain 2 g of added salt – that's one-third of the amount recommended a day.

Jordan also had a thick layer of butter on his toast.

That's a very healthy choice. There's plenty of fibre and protein in the beans, and carbohydrate from the bread.

d Suggest reasons why Jordan's meal was a healthy choice.

e Suggest reasons why Jordan's meal might not have been healthy.

f Would you consider doing any of the following? Give your reasons.

  (i) Paying extra for baked beans with reduced salt and sugar.

  (ii) Buying low-fat spread instead of butter.

  (iii) Baking your own bread.

Questions

1 Copy and complete these sentences.

  a Some scientists think that eating too much salt ...

  b Sugary foods cause ...

  c Eating too much fat ...

2 Many breakfast cereals contain more salt per 100 g than a packet of crisps. Which do you think is the healthier snack? Explain your answer.

3 Why is it a good idea to drink a glass of water with a sugary snack?

For your notes:

- Processed foods often contain a lot of salt and sugar.

- You need to look at foods very carefully to decide whether they are healthy or not.

7

A4 Total breakdown

Different sized particles

Each nutrient in our food is made up of particles. Carbohydrates, fats and proteins are all made of large particles. Vitamins and minerals are made of small ones. These particles are called **molecules**. You will learn more about molecules in Unit E Atoms and molecules.

The big molecules in carbohydrates, fats and proteins must be broken down into smaller ones before our bodies can use them. This is called **digestion**.

Digestion happens bit by bit as the food moves through your body.

The long journey

When you chew up and swallow your food, it begins its journey through a long tube from the mouth to the anus. The tube is called the **gut** and it is nine metres long.

The **digestive system** is all the organs that take part in digestion. They are shown in this diagram.

ⓐ **Look at the diagram. Name the part of the gut that links your mouth with your stomach.**

Breaking it down

As your food goes through the gut it is broken down into smaller molecules by chemicals called **enzymes**. These are added to the food in the mouth, stomach and small intestine.

Enzymes make the digestion of food happen more quickly. Without enzymes it could take a few days instead of a few hours to break down some foods.

ⓑ **What are enzymes?**

ⓒ **Why are enzymes important in digestion?**

Each enzyme helps break down a different type of nutrient. Some break down carbohydrates, some break down proteins and others break down fats.

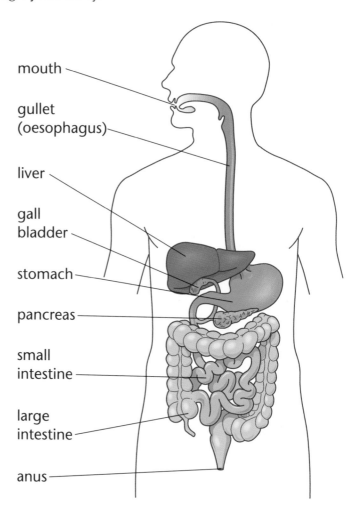

mouth
gullet (oesophagus)
liver
gall bladder
stomach
pancreas
small intestine
large intestine
anus

Beaumont's experiment

An interesting experiment started in 1922. Alexis St Martin was accidentally shot in the stomach. His recently eaten breakfast spilled out. The hole never healed properly and Dr William Beaumont sampled the stomach contents through the hole.

He tied a small piece of meat to the end of a silk string, dangled it through the hole in St Martin's stomach and pulled it out a couple of hours later to see if it had been digested! Dr Beaumont found the meat was digested quicker than the vegetables.

Enzymes in action

Starch is a carbohydrate found in rice, bread and pasta. It is an energy-giving food but it has large molecules.

The big starch molecules are made up of lots of little glucose molecules joined together. Enzymes break the starch molecule down into glucose molecules. You can think of enzymes as chemical scissors cutting up the big starch molecule.

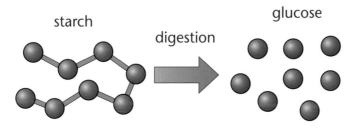

starch   glucose

digestion

d What happens to starch when it is digested?

Did you know?

Some washing powders are 'biological', and others are 'non-biological'. **Biological washing powders** contain enzymes. These break down stains on clothes caused by proteins in foods like egg or gravy. They digest the stains!

Questions

1 Match the correct beginnings and endings to write the sentences.

Beginnings	Endings
Carbohydrates, proteins and fats have …	… chemicals called enzymes
Digested foods in the small intestine have …	… big molecules
Food is digested by …	… small molecules

2 a Look at the diagram of the digestive system on page 8. Draw a flow chart to show the parts of the digestive system that food passes through in order, starting at the mouth.

b On your flow chart, say where enzymes are added to the food.

For your notes:

- **Digestion** takes place in the **digestive system**.

- Digestion is the breakdown of large food **molecules** into small food molecules.

- **Enzymes** speed up the breakdown of food.

- Different enzymes work on different nutrients.

A5 Taking it in

An absorbing process

When digested food gets to the small intestine it is made up of small molecules. These pass through the wall of the small intestine into the blood. This process is called **absorption**.

The blood takes the digested nutrients to every cell in the body where they can finally be used for energy and growth.

The small intestine has many features which make it good at absorbing food. It has a very thin wall with blood vessels running closely along the outside.

a **Where does the digested food go in your body?**

Getting through

How do molecules of digested food go through the intestine wall? This is where it is good to be small.

Look at the diagram on the right. Small molecules such as glucose can pass through tiny gaps in the wall of the small intestine. Large starch molecules cannot go through.

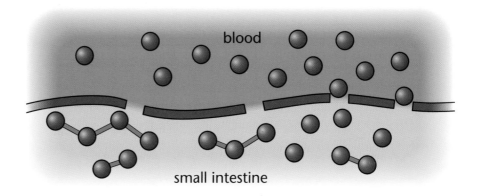

blood

small intestine

b **The idea of small fish and fishing nets is a model to help you imagine how absorption happens. Look at the picture of fish on the left. Which part of the model represents:**
(i) **large particles such as starch?**
(ii) **small particles such as glucose?**
(iii) **the wall of the small intestine?**

c **Why does food have to be digested?**

Some substances in food such as minerals and vitamins are already small enough to go straight through the gut wall.

Villi

Look at this photo. Inside the wall of the small intestine are millions of tiny finger-like structures called **villi**. The villi make the surface area of the small intestine much larger. The large surface makes sure that the digested food is absorbed quickly.

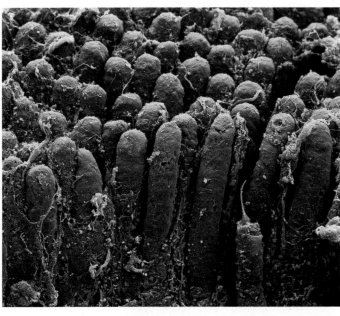

Passing through

Water and the fibre from our food are not digested, and are left in the small intestine. Fibre is not absorbed into the blood in the small intestine because its molecules are too big and we do not have the enzymes to help break it down.

The water and fibre pass into the **large intestine**. There water is absorbed back into the blood to be used by the body. The solid waste, called **faeces**, leaves the body through the **anus**. The waste is largely made up of fibre which has passed through the body unchanged. The process of getting rid of waste through the anus is called **egestion**.

d **Why is fibre not absorbed into the blood in the small intestine?**

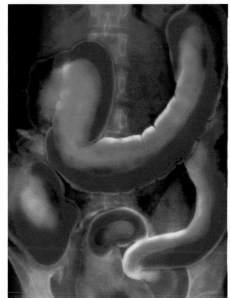

This X-ray shows the large intestine.

Questions

1 Where is digested food absorbed into the blood? Choose the correct answer.

   the stomach   the large intestine   the small intestine

2 Why do villi help absorption? Write out the correct answer.

   ● Food gets caught in their folds.

   ● They make the intestine wall into a big surface.

   ● They wave around and catch food as it goes through.

3 Explain why some substances can pass through the wall of the small intestine without being broken down.

4 What happens to fibre and water in the digestive system?

For your notes:

● Only small molecules can pass through the wall of the small intestine into the blood.

● Small molecules of digested food are **absorbed** into the blood.

A6 Chewing it over

Digestion of starch

Wendy took a bite of her baguette. She thought, 'The bigger the bite, the more starch there is to be digested, and the longer it takes …'.

Starch is broken down into glucose by an enzyme called salivary amylase. Wendy wanted to find out whether adding more of this enzyme to starch speeds up digestion.

She used the same amount of starch each time, but added different amounts of the enzyme. She used iodine indicator to show when the starch had disappeared. She timed how long it took for the starch to disappear each time. When the starch had disappeared, she knew it had all been digested.

enzyme   1%   2%   3%   4%   5%

When the iodine indicator loses its blue-black colour, all the starch has disappeared.

The input variable (the thing she changed) was the amount of enzyme. The outcome variable (the thing she measured) was the time taken to digest the starch. Her results are shown in the table.

Amount (concentration) of salivary amylase in %	Time taken to digest all the starch in seconds
1	240
2	210
3	160
4	115
5	80

Wendy wanted to see if there was a pattern in her results.
She drew a line graph. She put the input variable on the x-axis, along the bottom. She put the outcome variable on the y-axis, up the side. She plotted her results on the graph below.

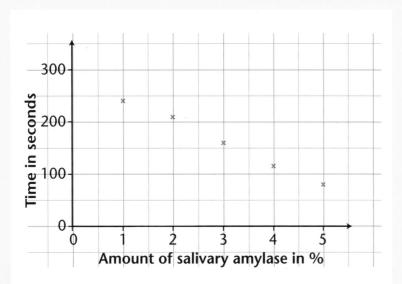

a Copy Wendy's graph. Try to draw a straight line on the graph to show the pattern of her results.

b Can you draw a straight line through all her crosses?

Lines of best fit

In many experiments, you cannot draw a line that passes through all the points. You have to draw a line that fits most of them. This is called the **line of best fit**.

Wendy and her friends were discussing why the graph may not go through all the points in an experiment.

We forgot to start the timer.

We forgot to watch the clock, and we took some readings a bit late.

Maybe some wells in the spotting tile were dirty.

We did the experiment all wrong.

Science experiments are always a bit inaccurate.

The timer was not accurate enough.

c Which of their ideas above might explain why the graph did not go through all the points?

The graph on the right is what Wendy's graph looked like when she had drawn in a line of best fit.

d What pattern do you see in the results?

e Describe the relationship between the input variable and the outcome variable.

f Why do you think that some of the points do not fit the pattern?

Interpreting graphs

Drawing a line of best fit helps you see the relationship shown by the graph. Once you have a line of best fit, you can read other results off it to make predictions.

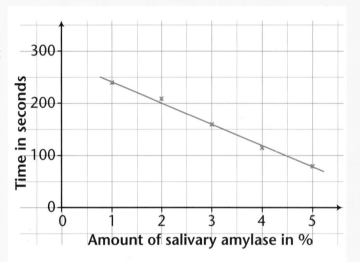

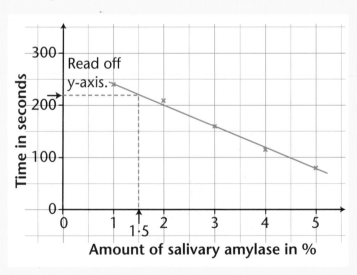

Wendy can now use the graph above to predict how long it would probably take for other amounts of salivary amylase to digest starch. She drew a line up to the graph from 1.5% on the x-axis, and read off the time on the y-axis. The graph on the left shows this.

g Why do you think she would want to do this?

Questions

1 Why do we use lines of best fit?

2 Sometimes all the results do not fit the pattern of the graph. Think about any experiments you have carried out in the past where the results were not what you expected. Why did this happen?

B1 Food for energy

Food and energy

Energy from the food you eat keeps your muscles moving and organs working. It is also used for growing and repairing cells. You need energy all the time to keep your body's life processes going, even when you are asleep. Food is like a fuel for the body.

Do you remember?

Energy comes from carbohydrates and is stored as fats. Carbohydrates, fats and proteins provide your body with most of the things you need to stay healthy.

ⓐ **What nutrients are the main sources of energy?**

The energy in the banana helps the tennis player to keep playing.

Body fuel

You have to burn fuels like petrol and gas to get energy from them. Fuels react with oxygen to produce carbon dioxide and water, and energy is released. Your body uses a similar reaction to get the energy from food. It is called **respiration**.

Respiration needs:

● glucose from the digestion of food

● oxygen from the air you breathe in.

Respiration produces:

● carbon dioxide in the air you breathe out

● water in the air you breathe out.

Respiration releases:

● **energy** to be used in your body.

Respiration takes place in all the cells in your body.

ⓑ **What is needed for respiration?**

ⓒ **Why do the cells in the body need to respire?**

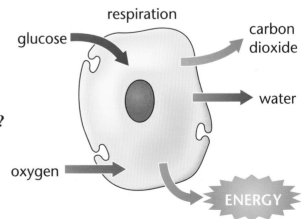

Working out

When you exercise hard your muscles need to release more energy from glucose, so your muscle cells respire more. This uses up a lot of glucose and oxygen. Your heart beats faster and you breathe more deeply to increase the supply of oxygen and glucose to the cells.

Most of the energy from respiration is transferred as movement energy in the muscles. Some of it is released as heat energy, which makes you feel hot.

d Why do you breathe more deeply when you exercise?

Most of the respiration your cells do needs oxygen. It is called **aerobic respiration**. But sometimes your body just can't supply enough oxygen to your cells. Then, for a short while, your cells can respire without oxygen. This happens when you run very fast for a long time. You get breathless and your muscles ache. You can get cramp and a 'stitch'. You pant to get more oxygen into your lungs and your muscles ache because the cells are respiring without oxygen.

e What happens to your body when your cells don't have enough oxygen to respire?

Questions

1 Copy and complete these sentences using the words below.

| cells | energy | glucose | water |

Respiration is the process by which humans get their _____. It takes place inside all _____. In respiration _____ reacts with oxygen to produce carbon dioxide and _____.

2 Give two or three things that the energy from respiration is used for.

3 Sometimes people chew glucose tablets just before they go into an exercise class. Why do you think they do this?

For your notes:

- **Aerobic respiration** is the process by which we get energy from food.

- In respiration, glucose reacts with oxygen to release energy and produce carbon dioxide and water.

- When not enough oxygen can get to the muscles, respiration happens without oxygen.

Energetic forests

A forest seems a very peaceful place. In fact, all the trees are very busy making their own food. This food is called glucose.

Like humans, plants need to release the energy from food by respiration. Respiration happens in all plant cells, just as it does in all animal cells. Glucose and oxygen react, producing carbon dioxide and water, and releasing energy.

ⓐ Where in a plant does respiration take place?

ⓑ Where do plants get the glucose needed for respiration?

Pea seeds

Miss Dupont decided to show to her pupils that plants respire. She set up an experiment with pea seeds just starting to grow. She told her pupils that the cells in the pea seeds respire to get energy for growth from food stored in the seeds.

She wanted to show that the respiring seeds produce carbon dioxide. She used an indicator which changes from red to yellow, even if only a very small amount of carbon dioxide is dissolved in it. The diagram shows the apparatus.

The indicator changed colour from red to yellow in tube 1 but not in tube 2.

ⓒ What did the pupils conclude from the experiment?

ⓓ Why did Miss Dupont set up tube 2?

Do you remember?

Like animals, plants need energy to carry out their life processes. Plants make their own food from air and water by using light energy.

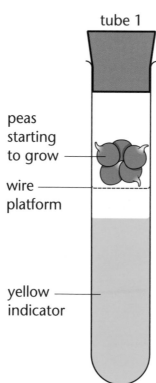
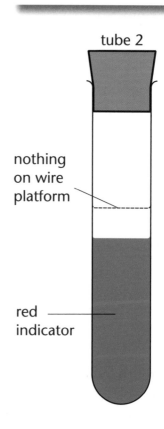

tube 1

tube 2

peas starting to grow

wire platform

nothing on wire platform

yellow indicator

red indicator

Maggots

Some of Miss Dupont's pupils had a further question about respiration.

They set up an experiment to find out whether maggots respire. They used the same indicator as they did in the pea seeds experiment. The diagram shows their apparatus after four hours.

Do small living things respire in the same way as humans and plants?

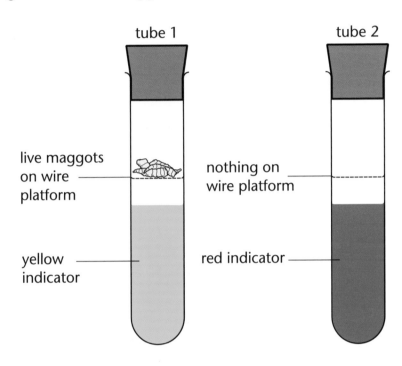

tube 1

tube 2

live maggots on wire platform

nothing on wire platform

yellow indicator

red indicator

e **Why did the indicator change colour in tube 1?**

At the end of the lesson, Miss Dupont's pupils concluded that all cells of all living things respire to release energy from food.

Questions

1 Copy and complete these sentences by choosing from the words below.

     cells   **energy**   **glucose**   **respiration**

Plants and animals release _____ from food. This process is called _____. It takes place in all living _____.

2 Which gas do plants use for respiration?

3 Describe a method of detecting the carbon dioxide released by cells.

For your notes:

- Plants and other organisms release energy from food by respiration, in the same way as humans do.

- Respiration takes place in every cell of all living things.

B3 Breathe in and out

Getting to the cells

All organisms need oxygen for respiration. For humans and other organisms that live on land, the oxygen comes from the air. Air needs to get inside the organisms to all the cells.

All cells produce carbon dioxide when they respire. This needs to get out of the organism into the air.

In plants and some very small animals, most cells are in contact with the air. Oxygen can pass straight into the cells, and carbon dioxide can pass out into the air.

In humans and other large animals, most cells are deep inside the body. They are not in contact with the air. We need a special way of getting oxygen into the cells for respiration, and carbon dioxide out. To do this we **breathe** air in and out of organs called lungs inside our bodies.

a **Where do all organisms get the oxygen they need for respiration?**

How do your lungs work?

If you put your hands on your chest, you can feel it move up and down as you breathe air in and out of your lungs.

The air we breathe

The graph shows how much oxygen and carbon dioxide there is in the air you breathe in and out.

air can get to all the cells in the leaf

Air is taken in through the nose and mouth

nose

mouth

left lung (cut open)

ribs

heart

right lung

left bronchus

Air reaches the tiny air sacs called alveoli

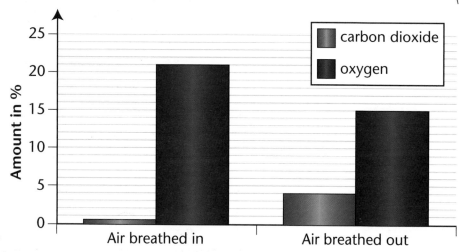

b **Compare the air you breathe in with the air you breathe out. Explain how it is different, and why.**

Oxygen in

This is how the oxygen you need for respiration gets from the air you breathe to the cells in your body.

1 Oxygen enters your body through the lungs when you breathe in air.

2 Inside the lungs are many tiny air sacs called **alveoli**. The alveoli walls are very thin. Gases move easily through them. Oxygen particles move out of the lungs through the walls of the alveoli.

3 The alveoli are surrounded by tiny blood vessels. Oxygen particles pass through the walls of the alveoli into the blood.

4 Blood carries oxygen to all cells in the body. Oxygen particles pass through the thin walls of the blood vessels into the cells where respiration takes place.

Carbon dioxide out

Carbon dioxide is a waste product of respiration. This is how the cells get rid of carbon dioxide.

5 Carbon dioxide particles move from the cells into the blood. They are carried back to the alveoli in the lungs.

6 Carbon dioxide particles pass out of the blood through the walls of the alveoli and into the lungs.

7 The carbon dioxide leaves your lungs in the air you breathe out.

c Which gas moves through the alveoli:
(i) from lungs to blood? (ii) from blood to lungs?

In your alveoli, the movement of oxygen into the blood and carbon dioxide out of the blood is called **gas exchange**.

d Which gas is there more of in the air you breathe out than the air you breathe in?

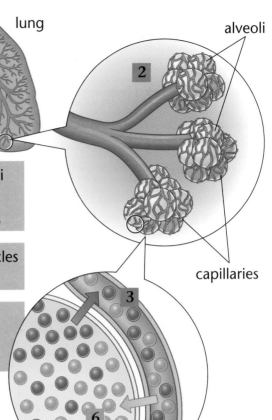

lung

alveoli

capillaries

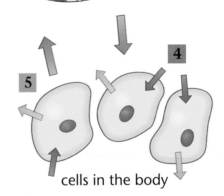

cells in the body

Questions

1 Describe the journey of an oxygen particle from the air into the blood, and a carbon dioxide particle from the blood to the air using the words below.

breathe in	breathe out	alveoli	blood	lungs
capillaries	thin walls	gas exchange	cells	

For your notes:

- Oxygen from the air enters the lungs and passes into the blood through the **alveoli**.

- Carbon dioxide moves from the blood, through the alveoli and into the lungs.

- The movement of gases in the alveoli is called **gas exchange**.

The transport link

In a city, roads link the places people need to travel to and from. Buses and cars travel along the roads carrying people.

Our bodies need a transport system like this to get blood to and from the cells. The blood carries oxygen, carbon dioxide and water.

The heart of the matter

The heart pumps blood round the body through blood vessels. The left and the right side of the heart pump separately. The left side has a thicker muscular wall to pump the blood all round the body.

The diagram below shows the path blood takes round the body.

- The left side of the heart pumps blood from the lungs to the body.

- The right side of the heart pumps blood from the body back to the lungs.

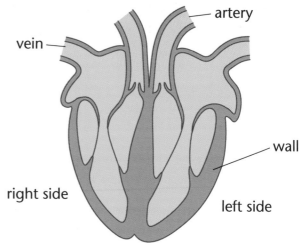

Do you remember?

The muscles in the walls of the heart contract regularly, pumping blood round the body. The blood vessels taking blood from the heart are called **arteries** and those returning it to the heart are called **veins**.

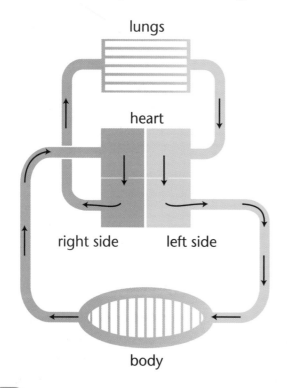

From the heart, blood goes to the lungs to collect oxygen. Then it goes back to the heart to be pumped round the body. The blood collects glucose from the digestive system and delivers oxygen and glucose to the cells. The blood collects carbon dioxide from the cells. It returns through the heart to deliver carbon dioxide to the lungs.

a Read the paragraph again. Follow the path it describes with your finger on the diagram.

b How many times does the blood pass through the heart on one circuit?

Blood vessels

Blood goes around the body in tubes called **blood vessels**.

- **Arteries** carry blood away from the heart.

- **Veins** carry blood back towards the heart.

- **Capillaries** connect arteries and veins. They carry the blood into organs and tissues.

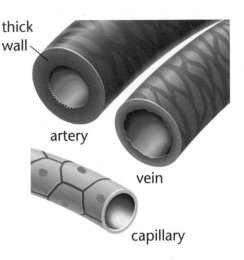

thick wall

artery

vein

capillary

Ideas have changed

We have known about the movement of the blood only since the 16th century. In ancient times, no one understood how the blood circulated around the body. Most theories were based on dissections of dead animals. Aristotle believed that the arteries were full of air because they are usually empty in dead bodies.

In 1628, William Harvey experimented on live animals. He showed that blood flowed out of the heart through arteries and came back through the veins. He demonstrated on humans that blood flows in one direction only. He explained this by suggesting that arteries and veins were connected by lots of tiny blood vessels or 'capillaries'. The blood could then go round in a circle. Valves in the blood vessels stop the blood flowing backwards.

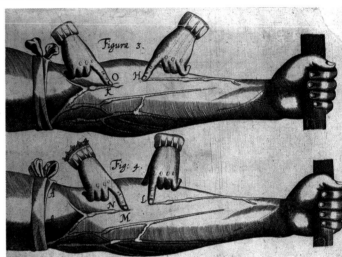

C What new evidence was available in the 17th century to disprove Aristotle's theory?

d How did Harvey explain how blood could flow in one direction only?

Questions

1 Copy and complete these sentences using the words below.

body   lungs

The left side of the heart pumps blood from the _____ to the _____.
The right side pumps blood from the _____ back up to the _____.

2 Write a sentence about each of these blood vessels:

arteries   veins   capillaries

3 Describe the journey of blood around the body, starting and finishing at the heart.

For your notes:

- The blood transports oxygen from the lungs to the cells, and carbon dioxide from the cells to the lungs.

- The heart is a muscular, double pump. One side supplies the lungs with blood; the other side supplies the body.

- Ideas about the movement of blood have changed because of new evidence.

Think about:

B5 Trouble with yeast

Special brew

Rosie Brown often told this story to her children.

Uncle William was famous in our village for his home-brewed beer. I was introduced to the process at a very early age.

He started by adding a tin of something called hops into a large barrel. Then he added lots of water and sugar. The final ingredient was some rather smelly granules called yeast. He left the mixture in the garage for a few weeks and then bottled it. The yeast made the beer fizz.

One year there was a huge disaster. William put the barrel in the airing cupboard instead of the garage. It fizzed so much that it exploded!

The investigation

Lauren was not sure what yeast was. She asked her friend Ryan. They decided to find an explanation for why yeast makes beer fizz.

Ryan's idea explaining why something happens is called a **hypothesis**.

Lauren was **predicting** what would happen if Ryan's hypothesis was right.

Ryan put some water, sugar and yeast in a bottle near the radiator. After a few hours it began to bubble.

Why does that happen?

I think that yeast is a chemical. It reacts with the sugar to make a gas.

OK, if you are right then the reaction should get faster if we heat up the mixture.

... It's like cooking – chemical reactions happen when food cooks, and food cooks quicker if you heat it up more.

Testing the hypothesis

Ryan and Lauren put the bottle with the yeast mixture on top of the radiator. It bubbled and frothed out of the bottle.

Then they boiled the mixture and carefully placed it back in the bottle on top of the radiator. Much to their surprise, it stopped bubbling completely. They needed to come up with a new hypothesis.

a What was Ryan's hypothesis?

b What was Lauren's prediction?

c What evidence supported Ryan's hypothesis?

d What evidence surprised Lauren and Ryan?

I was right!

Now let's see what happens if we boil the mixture in a saucepan first and then put it in the bottle – it should bubble really fast and explode!

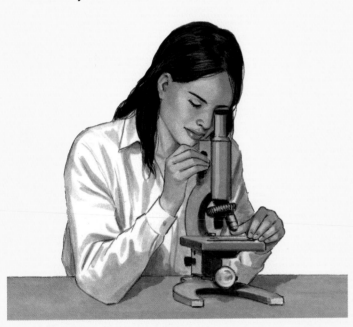

Back in class

Later, Lauren found out that yeast is a tiny fungus made of cells that can only be seen under the microscope. Just like any other living thing, yeast cells release energy from their food by respiration.

Another hypothesis sprang to mind – the yeast must have been feeding on the sugar. When the yeast cells respired, carbon dioxide was released. This caused the bubbling and frothing. When Lauren and Ryan boiled the yeast they must have killed it, and so respiration stopped. That is why the mixture stopped bubbling.

e What was Lauren's hypothesis?

Questions

Discuss these questions with your partner. Decide which is the correct word from each pair. Write down your answers.

1 An idea that explains why something happens is called a **hypothesis/prediction**.

2 Suggesting what will happen if your idea is right is called **investigating/predicting**.

3 To prove that your hypothesis is right, you need **evidence/ideas** to support it.

4 Can you think of another example where you have made a prediction to test a hypothesis in science? What evidence did you collect? Did it support your prediction?

C1 Going on growing

Unseen microorganisms

Some food goes mouldy if you leave it out in the air. You have probably seen blue-grey mould growing on old bread.

In 1881, Louis Pasteur proved that food decayed because 'germs' we can't see land on it from the air. Germs are tiny living things called **microorganisms**.

Do you remember?

Microorganisms feed, grow and reproduce like any other organism. Cells reproduce by dividing to make new cells.

A microorganism is a living thing that is so small we can only see it clearly with a microscope. Microorganisms are sometimes called **microbes**. Many of them are only a fraction of a millimetre long.

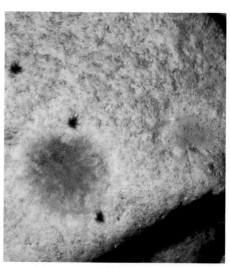
Mould growing on bread.

Types of microbe

There are very many different microorganisms, but there are three main types:

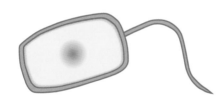

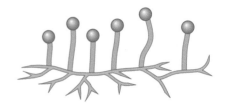

Bacteria are very small, usually about $\frac{1}{1000}$ mm across. A bacterium is a single-celled organism. They have a cell wall, but do not have a nucleus. They reproduce by dividing to make new cells.

Viruses are much smaller than bacteria. They are not made of cells.

Some **fungi**, such as yeast, are small, round and single celled. Others, like mould, are made of long threads.

ⓐ Give one way in which bacteria are similar to plant cells.

ⓑ Give one way in which bacteria are different from plant cells.

ⓒ Which are smaller, bacteria or viruses?

Useful microbes

The photos show some of the ways that microbes are useful to us.

Fungi are used to make products like those shown on the right.

Bacteria are used to make products like those shown below.

Yeast is used to make beer and wine.

Yeast makes bread rise.

Moulds are used to make medicines such as antibiotics.

Quorn is a made from fungi.

Moulds are used to make blue cheese.

Bacteria are used to make yoghurt and cheese.

Questions

1 Alex forgot to label the tabs on his index cards. Copy the cards below and add the correct label – bacteria, viruses or fungi – to each tab.

> very small
> single celled
> cell wall
> no nucleus

> extremely small
> not made of cells

2 Imagine that scientists have discovered a way to kill every single type of microbe on the planet. Write a story about how this would have a serious effect on our lives.

d Name two food products that are each made from:
(i) fungi
(ii) bacteria.

For your notes:

- There are three main groups of **microorganisms**: **bacteria**, **viruses** and **fungi**.

- **Microbes** can be very useful to us.

25

C2 Defence systems

Learn about:
- Microorganisms that cause disease
- How the body fights infection

Disease

The air around you is full of microbes. Your body is covered in them. Many microbes are harmless and most of the time you are healthy. But some microbes can cause **infections** or diseases if they get inside your body. You have probably had a cold or other infection at times.

Organisms that cause disease are called **pathogens**. The table shows some diseases caused by the different types of microbe. The photos show tuberculosis (**A**), chickenpox (**B**) and athlete's foot (**C**).

TB bacteria have damaged parts of the lungs (shown yellow) in this X-ray.

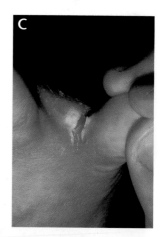

ⓐ   What is a pathogen?

How microbes enter the body

Your body is very good at keeping microbes out. The skin is a good barrier and stops microbes from getting into the blood. Tears contain a chemical that destroys bacteria. But there are several ways that microbes can get past these defences and enter your body.

ⓑ   List two ways in which your body keeps bacteria out.

Bacteria	Viruses	Fungi
meningitis (bacterial)	meningitis (viral)	athlete's foot
food poisoning	cold	ringworm
whooping cough	influenza ('flu)	
tetanus	chickenpox	
tuberculosis (TB)	German measles	
	rabies	
	AIDS	

Cuts in the skin allow microbes in.

Drinking water can carry microorganisms.

Sexually transmitted diseases, such as AIDS, can be caught from sexual intercourse without protection.

Food can contain harmful microorganisms.

Air has lots of microbes in it, which you can breathe in.

Animals can carry diseases and pass them on by biting you.

ⓒ   Why should you be concerned if you are bitten by a dog?

Fighting infection

Once microbes get inside your body, there is still another line of defence to fight them. This is called the **immune system**. In the blood, there are **white blood cells** to help in the fight against microbes. They are a vital part of the immune system.

White blood cells work in three different ways.

1 Some white blood cells can swallow up microbes.

2 White blood cells produce special chemicals called **antibodies** which attach themselves to the outside of the microbes and kill them.

3 White blood cells can destroy any poisonous chemicals produced by microbes.

An antibody is only able to recognise and fight one type of microbe. If your immune system has already met a microbe, the antibodies can be made more easily and your body can fight an infection a lot quicker. This makes you **immune** to the disease.

d (i) What is an antibody?

(ii) How does it fight infection?

Questions

1 Explain how the following situations can spread disease, using the words below to help you.

blood   air droplets   breathe   food

a Not washing your hands after going to the toilet.
b Sneezing in someone's face.
c Medicine users sharing syringes.

2 Survey your class to find out who has had chickenpox. Find out:

a How many people have had the disease once?
b How many have had the disease more than once?
c Why doesn't everyone keep on getting the disease?

3 Look at the cartoons on page 26. For each picture suggest a way of preventing the pathogens spreading.

For your notes:

● Organisms that cause infection are called **pathogens**.

● The first line of defence in the body is the skin.

● The **immune system** can fight off infection using **white blood cells** and **antibodies**.

Cleaning up

It is important to try to kill bacteria that are around us and on things we touch. In the home, many products contain substances that kill bacteria.

Food and drink

We also need to make sure bacteria don't get inside us in our food and drink. Chlorine is added to our drinking water to kill bacteria. We treat sewage and dispose of it safely to prevent it affecting our drinking water. Cooking food kills bacteria.

Antiseptics

We also need to stop bacteria getting inside us through cuts. You can stop a cut becoming infected by putting **antiseptic** cream on it. The cream contains chemicals that kill bacteria.

In 1867, the English doctor Joseph Lister first used an antiseptic. It was called carbolic acid and he used it when operating on people. It made it safer to have an operation because it stopped wounds becoming infected.

ⓐ **What are antiseptics used for?**

Sterilising solution kills bacteria in babies' bottles.

Antiperspirant kills the bacteria that cause body odour.

Disinfectant kills bacteria on floors and in sinks and toilets.

Toothpaste kills the bacteria that cause tooth decay.

Antiseptics kill bacteria outside our bodies.

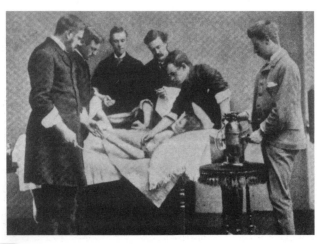

A carbolic acid spray being used during an operation in the 19th century.

Antibiotics

Alexander Fleming made one of the greatest medical breakthroughs by chance in 1928. Fleming was growing bacteria on an agar plate. Agar is a jelly used to grow bacteria. He noticed that some mould had got onto the **agar plate** and it was stopping the bacteria growing. He obtained a substance from the mould called penicillin. He found it could destroy several different bacteria.

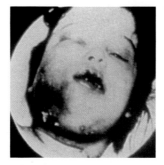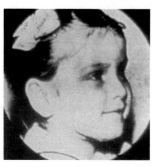

The first child to be treated with penicillin. Four weeks after treatment the infection was gone.

Penicillin is an **antibiotic**. Antibiotics are medicines that kill bacteria that have got inside the body. None of them will kill viruses. This is why your doctor may give you an antibiotic for a sore throat, but not for chickenpox.

b What is penicillin made from?

c Which of the diseases below should be treated with antibiotics?

> *whooping cough   German measles*
> *a cold   'flu   rabies   tetanus*

More antibiotics

Since Fleming discovered penicillin, a large number of other antibiotics have been developed. Some of these are shown in the photo opposite.

Antibiotics are not medicines that you can buy over the counter. They must be prescribed by your doctor. Each type of antibiotic will kill only certain bacteria. It is important for doctors to prescribe the right one.

d Why do you think that some doctors will not prescribe antibiotics over the phone?

Questions

1 Copy and complete these sentences.

An antiseptic is …   An antibiotic is …

2 Explain why people are not prescribed antibiotics if they have colds or 'flu.

3 How did the discoveries of the scientists below help to protect people against infectious diseases?

a Lister   **b** Fleming.

For your notes:

- **Antiseptics** contain substances that kill bacteria.

- **Antibiotics** are medicines that kill bacteria, but they have no effect on viruses.

C4 Fighting infection

A helping hand

Once your immune system has met a microbe and made antibodies against it, you are protected. But there is a way to become protected without having to catch every disease to make your immune system work!

Dead or inactive microbes can be injected into your body. The injection is called a **vaccination**. It does not make you ill, but your body produces antibodies against the microbes. These antibodies are then ready in case the disease ever infects your body. You have been **immunised**.

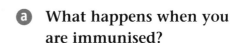 **What happens when you are immunised?**

Lady Mary Wortley Montague

In the eighteenth century people were very afraid of catching smallpox. People who caught it were very ill. They had sores full of pus all over their body and usually died.

In 1721, Lady Montague introduced to Britain a way of immunising people against smallpox. Some of the pus from a smallpox sore was put into a cut made in the vein of a healthy person. It gave them a small dose of the disease and when they recovered they were immune to the disease. But sometimes things went wrong and the person died.

Lady Montague.

b Why was this method of immunising people against smallpox risky?

Edward Jenner's discovery

Read the story about Jenner on the opposite page then answer the questions on the right.

Jenner gained support for his work from the Royal Family. In 1853, all children in Britain were vaccinated against smallpox. Smallpox has now been wiped out completely worldwide.

Many more diseases, such as measles, mumps and rubella, could be wiped out by vaccinating all children.

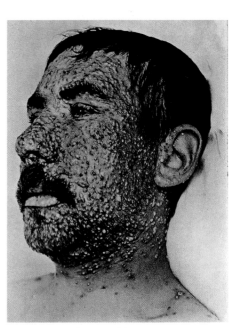
A man with smallpox.

c What was Edward Jenner's theory?

d Why was James Phipps important?

e Would Jenner's experiment be allowed today? Give a reason for your answer.

I'm Edward Jenner. While I was working in Gloucestershire in 1788 there was a terrible outbreak of smallpox. Many people died. But I noticed that people who worked with cows caught a much milder disease called cowpox. They never seemed to get smallpox.

One day, a milkmaid came to see me. She had blisters on her hands caused by cowpox caught from the cows. I took some of the pus from one of her sores.

I went to see a local farmer called Phipps.

I would like to try something out on your son. I'll scratch his skin and put cowpox pus into him. Then later I'll do the same with smallpox pus to check out my theory.

James Phipps suffered from cowpox and soon recovered. Six weeks later, I visited James again. This time I used smallpox pus, but he did not suffer from smallpox. The cowpox had made him immune to smallpox. I called my discovery vaccination.

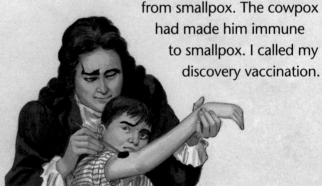

Questions

1 Write out the name of each person along with the correct thing they are famous for.

Name	Famous for…
Lady Montague	discovering that having cowpox made people immune to smallpox
James Phipps	introducing to Britain a way of immunising people against smallpox
Edward Jenner	being given cowpox pus and then smallpox pus but did not catch smallpox

2 Explain the meaning of the word vaccination.

3 Imagine you are James Phipps having a conversation with Edward Jenner. Write down some of the questions you might ask.

4 Jenner's story could have ended differently if James had caught smallpox. Write a different end to his story.

5 Make a list of the vaccinations you have had.

For your notes:

- The immune system can be helped by **vaccination**.

- Dead or inactive microbes can be injected into your body so your body produces antibodies against them.

- These antibodies are then ready in case the disease infects your body.

C5 The battle goes on

The story of Eyam

The nursery rhyme on the right is about bubonic plague. This was a deadly disease caused by a bacterium that infected rats. The fleas that lived on the rats passed the disease to humans when they bit them. It then spread from person to person by coughs and sneezes. People used to believe that carrying a posy of flowers close to the nose would keep away the disease.

*Ring a ring of roses
A pocket full of posies
Atishoo! Atishoo!
We all fall down!*

a How is bubonic plague passed to humans?

In 1665 the Great Plague spread through London killing thousands of people. One day a box of laundry was brought to the village of Eyam in Derbyshire by a traveller from London.
The laundry had fleas in it and the plague broke out in the village. More than three-quarters of the people of Eyam died.

The plague would have spread beyond the village, but a brave vicar called William Mompesson persuaded the villagers to stay in the village to contain the disease. Their food and supplies were delivered to the edge of the village. They used to drop money into the well for the delivery people to avoid spreading the infection on the coins.

The village of Eyam today.

b What stopped the plague spreading out of Eyam?

Recent outbreaks

The last plague outbreak happened in the United States in 1924. Since then there have been just a few cases a year in areas with poor housing and rats. Today, people with the disease are cared for in hospital, isolated from other patients, and given antibiotics.

c How is bubonic plague controlled now?

Dr Snow's discovery

If you want to control a disease, it is important to find out how it is spread.

In 1848, Dr John Snow worked in London. There was a bad outbreak of cholera in the area shown on this map. Cholera is caused by a bacterium. At that time, the people got their drinking water from pumps in the street. On a map, Dr Snow showed the pumps and where the victims lived. He found that many of the victims lived near one pump. He suggested that the water from the pump was giving cholera to the people. He closed the pump and there were no new cases.

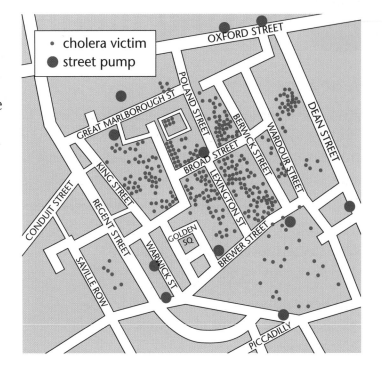

d **Look at the map on the right. Which pump do you think Dr Snow closed?**

People collecting water from a pump in Bangladesh.

Our water supply has chlorine added to it to kill bacteria. Cholera is still a problem in areas where people get their water from shared wells and sewage might get into the drinking water. The spread of cholera in these areas is controlled by:

- adding chlorine to wells
- boiling water
- immunisation
- using antibiotics.

e **What is added to our water supply to kill bacteria?**

For your notes:

- Scientists use evidence to tackle the spread of disease in different ways.

- William Mompesson persuaded the villagers of Eyam to stay in their village to contain the plague.

- Dr John Snow discovered that cholera was spread by drinking infected water.

Questions

1 Which disease is transmitted to humans by:

   a water?   **b** fleas?

2 Imagine you are living in Eyam in 1665. Design a poster to warn your fellow villagers of the danger they face, and to give advice about what to do.

3 Make a time line of all the medical breakthroughs mentioned on these two pages.

C6 Testing medicines

A new medicine

How do scientists design new medicines? They start by looking at what causes disease and how it affects the body. This gives them clues about which chemicals might help to treat the disease.

New medicines are first tested on animals and then on human volunteers to make sure they are safe. Only then can medicines be given by doctors to any patient that needs them.

ⓐ **Why do you think so much testing is needed before medicines are used on patients?**

Correlation

The scientists need to see if the medicine is going to make patients get better. They want to see if there is a link, or a **correlation**, between the patient taking the medicine and getting better. No correlation means there is no link – the medicine does not make the patient get better.

Scientists divide the patients into two groups. One group is given the new medicine, and the other group is given a **placebo**. A placebo acts as a **control** – it does not contain any medicine at all.

ⓑ **Why do you think the control patients are given a placebo instead of being given no treatment at all?**

There are three types of correlation.

● If the medicine works, then there is a **positive correlation**.

● If the medicine does not work, then there is a **negative correlation**.

● If the numbers of people getting better and not getting better are the same, then there is no correlation.

A new medicine

Dr Franklin was testing a medicine to treat a type of influenza. She tested 40 patients.

● 20 were given medicine B182.

● 20 were given a placebo.

These were the results.

Of the 20 patients given medicine B182, 15 showed a positive effect (an improvement) and 5 showed no effect.

Of the 20 patients given the placebo, 1 patient showed a positive effect and 19 showed no effect.

To see if there is a correlation between taking medicine B182 and getting better, we use a table like the one below.

The 15 people in box A proved that the medicine worked because most of the people treated with the medicine got better. The 19 people in box D also proved that the new medicine worked because most of the people who were not treated with the medicine did not get better.

	Treated	Not treated
positive effect	A 15	B 1
no effect	C 5	D 19

To find out what the correlation is in the results, we calculate the ratio between A + D and C + B.

A + D : C + B = (15 + 19) : (5 + 1)

$\qquad$ = 34 : 6

If the numbers in the yellow boxes add up to more than the numbers in the brown boxes then there is a positive correlation.

If the numbers in the yellow boxes add up to less than the numbers in the brown boxes there is a negative correlation.

If the numbers are the same then there is no correlation.

c How many people's results suggested the medicine didn't work?

d What type of correlation can you see in the example above?

e What does this test tell you about medicine B182?

Questions

1 Dr Franklin decided to repeat her experiment in another part of the country. Why do you think she did this?

2 Do you think the sample size in the trial was big enough?

3 What do you think Dr Franklin's team should do next?

D1 Plant groups

Sorting them out

There are millions of species of plants. They make up a large part of the environment, providing food and shelter for animals. Scientists classify the millions of plant species into groups to make them easier to study.

One way to start to classify plants is by looking at how they **reproduce**. To reproduce, two groups of plants make **seeds** and two groups make **spores**.

Another way is by looking at the leaves. Some plants have leaves with a waterproof waxy layer called a **cuticle** on their top surface to keep in water. We can also look at if they have **veins** to carry water.

Do you remember?

Living things are sorted into groups with similar features. This is called classifying. Animals can be classified as vertebrates or invertebrates.

Flowering plants

The biggest group of plants is the **flowering plants**. These include grasses and many trees. Flowering plants reproduce by making seeds inside the flowers.

Flowering plants have leaves with cuticles. They also have veins to carry water through the plant. Flowering plants can grow in dry places where many other plants would fail. This is because they have good systems for reproduction and for carrying and keeping in water.

Grasses are flowering plants.

Silver birch trees are flowering plants.

a What are flowers for?

Conifers

Conifers are trees with a large trunk and large roots. Conifers make seeds inside **cones**. They have thin needle-like leaves with a cuticle, and they have veins to transport water. Conifers can live in very cold, frozen climates.

Did you know?

The largest land habitat in the world is coniferous forest.

Conifers.

Ferns

Ferns make spores. They need water for this. Ferns have large, tough leaves called **fronds** which have cuticles. They also have strong stems and veins to carry water. Ferns grow well in damp, cool, shaded woodland habitats.

Ferns.

Mosses

Mosses also make spores. They are small plants that look like a springy cushion. They have very small, simple leaves with no cuticles. They do not have veins to carry water. Mosses dry out easily. This is why they have to live in wet places.

Mosses.

b Why would you be more likely to find mosses growing near a duck pond under an oak tree than in the middle of a field?

c (i) Copy and complete this flow chart showing how we can classify plants.

(ii) Another way of classifying plants could be to start by putting them into two groups: 'have veins to transport water' and 'have no veins'. Draw another flow chart to show how these two groups could be divided into flowering plants, conifers, ferns and mosses.

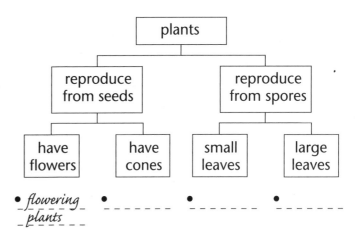

plants

reproduce from seeds — reproduce from spores

have flowers — have cones — small leaves — large leaves

• *flowering plants*   • _ _ _ _ _ _   • _ _ _ _ _ _   • _ _ _ _ _ _

Questions

1 Copy and complete these sentences by choosing from the words below.

**conifers   dry   ferns   flowers   mosses
seeds   spores   wet   flowering**

The _____ plants are the only group of plants that have _____. Like the _____, they reproduce by making _____.
The _____ dry out easily and so are found in _____ places.

2 Which type of forest would you expect to find in the Swiss Alps?

3 Which plant groups can survive in most land habitats? Give a reason for your answer.

For your notes:

- Plants are classified into four groups by looking at how they **reproduce**, whether the leaves have **cuticles** and how they carry water.

- The four groups are **flowering plants, conifers, ferns** and **mosses**.

D2 A place to live

Ecosystems

A wood has lots of shade. The air is often cool and moist. Trees provide good nesting sites for birds. There are lots of nuts and berries for them to eat in the autumn. The wood provides everything that the organisms in it need for their life processes.

An **ecosystem** is a habitat along with all the living things in it, as well as its soil, air and climate.

Different habitats

A habitat might be on land or in water. Examples of land habitats include fields, forests, soil and deserts. Water habitats include ponds, rivers or lakes and even salty water like the sea.

A habitat can be: ● hot or cold ● wet or dry ● light or dark.

a **Make a list of the environmental conditions you might measure if you were studying a habitat.**

Plants and animals have **adaptations** that help them to survive in different habitats.

Pond life

Becky and Parveen investigated a pond habitat. They wanted to find out whether there was a link between oxygen levels and the types of organism. Look at these photos. They used sensors connected to a datalogger to measure the amount of oxygen in the school pond.

They also used **pond dipping** to find out what organisms could live in different parts of the pond.

They took samples of water from the:

● surface ● side ● middle ● bottom.

b **What did Becky and Parveen investigate?**

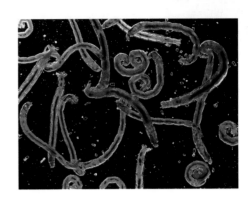

They found there was most oxygen in the surface water and least in the water near the muddy bottom of the pond. On the surface, they found lots of insects. The only organisms they found at the bottom of the pond were bloodworms.

Look at the photo on the right of bloodworms, taken under a microscope. They have a red substance in their blood that joins with oxygen. This means a bloodworm can survive at the bottom of the pond where there is very little oxygen.

c What feature of the bloodworm lets it survive in water that has very little oxygen?

Barnacles cement themselves to rocks.

Sea shells

Gavin and Ian investigated a seashore habitat. They wanted to find out how the animals living on the rocky shore were adapted to survive the force of the waves when the tide comes in.

Most of the animas they found had thick shells to protect them. Some had ways of attaching themselves firmly to the rocks so that they are not washed away.

d How are barnacles in the picture on the left adapted to survive the tides?

Questions

1 This photo shows a very different ecosystem – a city.

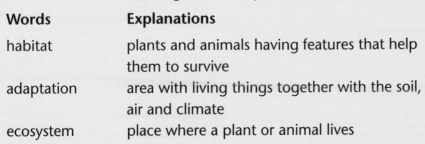

Describe what this ecosystem is like. Think about:

- the air
- the temperature
- the food available for animals
- the space for animals to live.

2 Write out each word along with its explanation.

Words	Explanations
habitat	plants and animals having features that help them to survive
adaptation	area with living things together with the soil, air and climate
ecosystem	place where a plant or animal lives

3 A pond is about to be filled in, in the school grounds, to extend the sports hall. How would you feel about this? What would you do?

For your notes:

- A **habitat** on land or in water has environmental conditions that can be measured.

- Plants and animals have features called **adaptations** that help them to survive.

- An **ecosystem** is a habitat together with its living things, the soil, air and climate.

D3 Home alone?

Beachcombing

If you are walking along the beach you might be tempted to see what organisms you can find in a rock pool. You will see different shellfish feeding on the seaweed. If you are patient, you might see the second link in a food chain – a crab ready to eat a mussel.

a What organism might a crab be eaten by?

A food chain shows the feeding relationships between the organisms in an ecosystem. Most food chains start with a plant, or producer. The plant makes its own food from carbon dioxide, water and light energy from the Sun. When the mussels eat the seaweed the energy in the seaweed is transferred to the mussel.

Do you remember?

The arrows in a **food chain** show what eats what, and the direction of the energy transfer.

b Look at this food chain. Which organism is:
   (i) a producer?
   (ii) a herbivore?
   (iii) a carnivore?

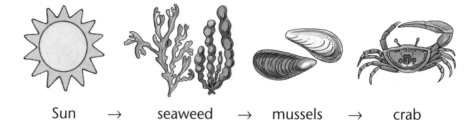

Sun → seaweed → mussels → crab

Pyramids of numbers

Lots of seaweed will feed a mussel. Several mussels will feed just one crab. If you look at the number of producers, herbivores and carnivores in this food chain, you can build a pyramid.

c What happens to the number of consumers as you go up the pyramid?

To make the pyramid clearer we can count the numbers of crabs, mussels and seaweed plants in an ecosystem. We draw bars of different lengths to represent the numbers of organisms. We call this a **pyramid of numbers.**

crabs

mussels

seaweed

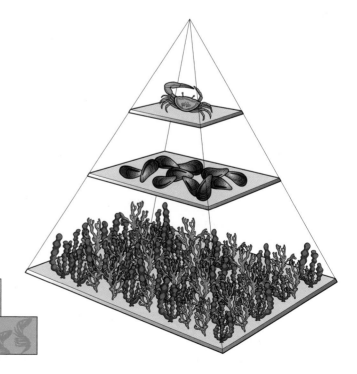

Food webs

Lots of food chains link together to make a **food web**. In this food web, both seals and seagulls eat crabs.

d How many food chains can you find in this food web? Write them out.

Crabs are predators. Mussels are prey for crabs. Humans also like to eat mussels. In some places people catch large numbers of mussels to sell in fish markets.

e If lots of mussels are caught, what do you think could happen to the:
(i) crabs? (ii) winkles?

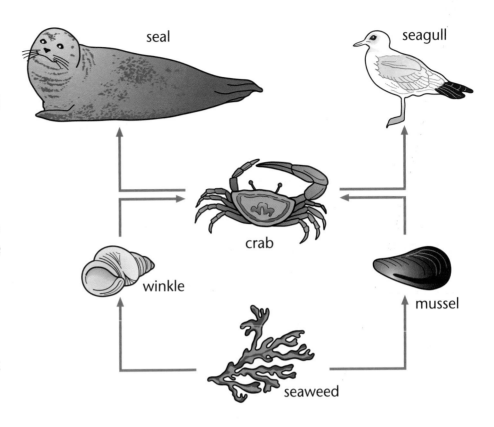

seal

seagull

crab

winkle

mussel

seaweed

Dead bodies

Animals get nutrients by eating plants and animals. Plants need nutrients too. They get minerals from soil or water.

Bacteria and fungi live in rock pools, in rivers and in soil. They feed on the waste products and dead bodies of plants and animals. They break them down to useful nutrients that plants need. Bacteria and fungi are called **decomposers**.

Questions

1 Copy and complete these sentences by choosing from the words below.

     chain   consumers   carnivores   herbivores
          producers   pyramid   web

A food _____ has lots of food _____ linked together. If you count the numbers of _____, _____ and _____ in a food chain, you can build a _____. The number of _____ decreases as you go up the pyramid.

2 Explain why food chains start with a green plant.

3 How do plants use the waste products and the decayed bodies of other organisms?

For your notes:

- If we count the number of organisms at each level of a **food chain**, we can draw a **pyramid of numbers**.

- **Decomposers** break down the waste and dead bodies of other organisms into useful nutrients that plants need.

D4 Populations

On Onkar

In any habitat, we find lots of species. The number of organisms of a particular species living in a habitat is called the **population**.

a **Read about conditions on Onkar. Then list all the things the gimbuls had for their life processes.**

Conditions on Onkar

The moon Onkar orbits the outer planet of a distant galaxy. Conditions on Onkar are very similar to those on Earth. Luhans live there. They are like humans but they live in underground cities away from natural light. Their skin is very sensitive to light.

On the ground above the cities, the luhans hunt small mammals called gimbuls to eat. The gimbuls feed on grass and the seeds of the red zetta plant in the early morning. They drink water from puddles.

A pair of gimbuls nested in a disused building using dry vegetation from among the ruins. The gimbuls ate well and reproduced. They were well hidden from the wooks who might eat them.

The gimbuls had everything they needed. The number of gimbuls in the building grew to a population of 102 after 35 weeks!

Soon things began to go wrong for the gimbuls in the disused building. Death and disease became widespread.

b **Why do you think the gimbuls were dying?**

Competition

If the population grows a lot, there is **competition** between the organisms in a habitat for the resources they need. For the gimbuls:

- the food was running out

- there wasn't enough clean water

- the building was overcrowded and very dirty, so diseases were being passed on.

Wooks on the look-out

A wook noticed all the gimbuls running in and out of the disused building. He was hungry and ready to attack the gimbuls at dawn. Wooks had always eaten a few gimbuls. Now there were so many gimbuls that they became the main food for the wook. Only the gimbuls that were the strongest and fastest runners escaped the wooks.

c Which animals were prey?

d Which animals were predators?

Predation

Predation, or being caught and eaten by a predator, is a problem for many organisms. The fittest and strongest prey animals escape if they are lucky.

A change in population

Look at the table below showing how the gimbul population in the building changed over 40 weeks.

Time in weeks	0	5	10	15	20	25	30	35	40
Number of gimbuls	2	8	19	34	65	93	99	102	102

e When did the population growth begin to slow down?

f Which four factors were causing the population growth to slow down?

All interdependent

The size of any population depends on competition between the members of that species for food, water and space. It also depends on how many of them are eaten by predators or killed by disease. The different species in a habitat are all **interdependent**. When there are lots of gimbuls the wooks eat well and reproduce. If the gimbul population decreases, so will the wook population.

Questions

1 Copy and complete these sentences by choosing from the words below.

> habitat   competition   compete   resources
> food   space   species   water

The size of a population is affected by _____. Animals _____ for the _____ they need, such as _____, _____ and _____.

2 On Onkar:

  a Why were the gimbuls only eaten by the luhans at night?
  b Why did the gimbuls become the main food for the wooks?
  c If the population of gimbuls decreases, what will happen to the luhans?

For your notes:

- A **population** is the number of individuals of a species living in a habitat.

- **Competition** for resources such as food, water and space, predation and disease all affect the size of a population.

43

Not many left?

Pupils Joan and Lydia think they have found a rare variety of daisy among the normal daisies in a field. The daisy has a bright pink tinge to its petals and grows well in moist conditions. There are plans to build a petrol station on the field.

Look at the map of the field on the right. On the map, 1 mm represents 1 m of the field.

There are 1000 mm in a metre, so 1 mm on the map means 1000 mm in the field. We call this a **ratio** of 1:1000. Any measurements on the map need to be multiplied by 1000 to give the real distance in the field.

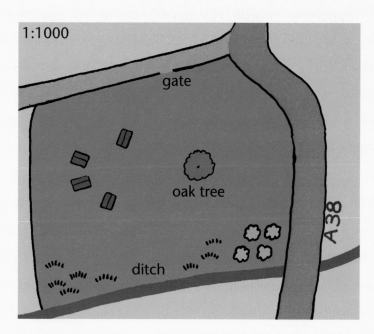

1:1000

gate

oak tree

ditch

A38

ⓐ **Measure the distance from the gate to the middle of the largest oak tree on the map.**

To find the real distance you multiply this by 1000.

ⓑ **Work out the real distance in metres from the gate to the oak tree.**

The Northfield Conservation Group wants to find out how many of the rare daisy plants are in the field. The evidence from their work might save the area from the developers. Joan and Lydia were discussing how to count the plants:

Let's just count all the special daisy plants in the field.

I think it would be better to look at a few small areas as samples.

We could find an area with lots of the daisies and do our samples there.

But that wouldn't tell us the total number in the field.

Random sampling

Joan and Lydia decided that the fairest way of finding out how many special daisy plants there are in the field was to do **random samples**. This means doing samples in different places without choosing the places deliberately.

c **Why do you think they decided not to count every single rare daisy plant in the field?**

Look at the top photo. Joan and Lydia used a **quadrat** to do their sampling. This is a wooden frame measuring one metre on all four sides. This means it has an area of one square metre.

Joan threw a quadrat over her shoulder without looking where it would land. Then she wrote down the number of rare daisy plants inside the quadrat.

She threw the quadrat and counted the daisy plants 10 times.

d **Why did Joan throw the quadrat without looking where it would land?**

Joan threw the quadrat down 10 times. Her sample was 10 times one square metre, so it was 10 square metres.

Joan's results

Joan and Lydia found 9 rare daisy plants in Joan's sample.

The whole sample has an area of 10 square metres. The field covers 4000 square metres in total. So the ratio of the area they sampled to the whole field is 1:400.

The ratio of the number of plants in the sample to the number of plants in the field is the same, 1:400. So to find the number of plants in the whole field, they multiplied the number in the sample by 400.

e **How many rare daisy plants did Joan and Lydia think might be in the field?**

f **Will this be the exact number of plants in the field?**

Throw number	Number of rare daisy plants
1	0
2	0
3	0
4	3
5	0
6	0
7	0
8	0
9	0
10	6

Questions

1 a How accurate do you think Joan and Lydia's experiments were?

b How could they have made the experiments more reliable? Think about where the special daisy prefers to grow.

E1 It's elementary

Too many

There are too many different materials to count. Look at the photo. There are hundreds of materials just in this photo.

a Name four materials shown in the photo.

Making sense of so many materials is hard. It has taken scientists thousands of years. This is because most materials are **mixtures** of substances. It is difficult to separate some mixtures into **pure** substances.

Gold

Gold is a beautiful, buttery yellow. In the past, the more gold you had, the richer you were. Even today, gold still has value all over the world.

Jabir ibn-Hayyan was an Arab scientist. He lived between 760 and 815 AD. Like many early scientists, he wanted to make gold. He thought that you could make gold by mixing mercury and sulphur.

Unfortunately, this isn't true. You can get gold from rocks, but the gold particles are already there.

b Why did Jabir ibn-Hayyan want to make gold?

c Why didn't his idea work?

Elements

Gold is an **element**. You cannot break down an element into anything simpler. Filtering and distilling do not break down gold. Chemical reactions cannot break down gold. Gold is gold.

Scientists have identified many elements. Mercury and sulphur are elements. So are silver, oxygen, helium and hydrogen.

What makes an element?

An element contains only one type of **atom**. An atom is the simplest type of particle.

ⓓ **The diagram shows different substances. Two are elements and one is a mixture. Which of A, B or C are elements?**

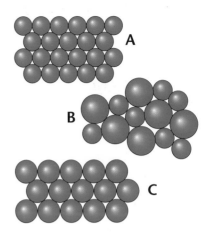

Sometimes atoms go around on their own. Helium does this.

Sometimes atoms of elements go around in groups. For example, oxygen atoms join to make pairs. These groups of atoms are called **molecules**.

The word **particle** can be used for an atom or a molecule, like the word 'child' can be used for a boy or a girl.

helium atoms

oxygen atoms

Elements around us

We find very few pure elements in our surroundings. Gold is found as small lumps of pure gold. Sulphur is found near volcanoes.

Other elements have to be separated from mixtures or made by chemical reactions.

'Panning' for gold.

The yellow solid is sulphur.

Questions

1 Look at 'For your notes' on the right. Copy and complete these sentences.

Some pure substances cannot be broken down using chemical reactions. These are called _____. They contain only one type of _____.

2 Look at the diagram. It shows six different pure substances. Which of the substances are elements?

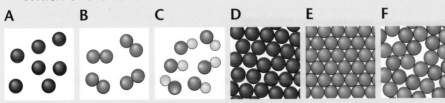

3 List all the elements on these pages.

4 Sometimes people who are ill need to breathe pure oxygen. Where could we get the element oxygen from?

For your notes:

- Most materials are **mixtures**. Mixtures can be separated into **pure** substances.

- Some pure substances are **elements**. Elements cannot be broken down, even with chemical reactions.

- Elements contain only one type of **atom**.

- A **molecule** is a group of atoms joined together. Some elements are molecules.

Learn about:
- Symbols for elements
- The periodic table

E2 The elements

Every element has a symbol

People across the world speak different languages. The word for iron is different in each language. But scientists across the world can understand each other because they all use the same **symbol** for iron, Fe.

There are some rules for symbols.

- The first letter is a capital letter.

- If there is a second letter, it is a small letter.

a What is the symbol for iron?

Some elements have been known from ancient times. The symbol for iron, Fe, comes from the Latin word for iron (ferrum). Latin was the language spoken by the Romans. Gold has the symbol Au, from the Latin word for gold (aurum).

b Calcium, cobalt and copper are all elements starting with C. Match the symbols below with these elements.
(*Hint:* the Latin name for copper was cuprum.)

Cu   Ca   Co

Putting the elements in order

There are 113 elements. Learning about 113 different elements is difficult. We put all the elements in a special table to make it easier. This table is called the **periodic table**. Most of it is shown on the opposite page.

Look at the vertical columns in the periodic table. They are labelled I, II, III, IV, V, VI, VII and 0. These are called **groups**. The elements in a group are alike.

Look at the horizontal rows in the periodic table. They are labelled 1, 2, 3, 4, 5, 6 and 7. These are called **periods**.

Most elements are **metals**. Some elements are not; these are called **non-metals**.

c Where are the metals in the periodic table? Are they to the left or to the right as you look at the table?

d Are the elements in Group II metals or non-metals?

e How many non-metals are there in the same period as oxygen?

																H	

I	II	Groups	III	IV	V	VI	VII	0 He	Period

Table (periodic table):

I	II											III	IV	V	VI	VII	0	Periods
																	He	1
Li	Be											B	C	N	O	F	Ne	2
Na	Mg											Al	Si	P	S	Cl	Ar	3
K	Ca	Sc	Ti	V	Cr	Mn	Fe	Co	Ni	Cu	Zn	Ga	Ge	As	Se	Br	Kr	4
Rb	Sr	Y	Zr	Nb	Mo	Tc	Ru	Rh	Pd	Ag	Cd	In	Sn	Sb	Te	I	Xe	5
Cs	Ba	La	Hf	Ta	W	Re	Os	Ir	Pt	Au	Hg	Tl	Pb	Bi	Po	At	Rn	6
Fr	Ra	Ac																7

Key

■ metals

□ non-metals

Finding a pattern

By 1860 scientists knew about 61 different elements. Discovering an element made you famous. Scientists struggled to find any patterns in the elements.

In 1860 there was the first international meeting for scientists studying chemistry. Some scientists started putting the elements in order, using the mass of their atoms. Hydrogen, with the lightest atoms, was first. The race had started to find a useful way of classifying the elements. Different patterns were suggested, but the one suggested by Dmitri Ivanovich Mendeléev, was the most useful. He put elements with similar properties in the same group. Mendeléev's pattern became the basis of the periodic table we use today.

Questions

1 What do we call:

  a a substance with one type of atom?
  b the letters that stand for an element?

2 Imagine that each symbol has only one letter.

  a How many different letters are there in the alphabet?
  b How many different symbols could there be?
  c How many elements are there?
  d Would there be enough symbols?

3 Find the symbols for these metals.

  a magnesium **b** nickel **c** zinc **d** aluminium.

4 Find the symbols for these non-metals.

  a fluorine **b** nitrogen **c** sulphur **d** neon.

For your notes:

- There are over one hundred **elements**.
- Each element has a **symbol**.
- We arrange the elements in the **periodic table**.

How elements differ

What are they like?

When scientists put the elements into the periodic table, they found that elements in the same group looked and reacted in similar ways. How elements look and react are called their **properties**.

The first things you notice when you study elements are how they look and if they are solid, liquid or gas.

How do they look?

Kay's class was looking at the appearances of elements. The class agreed that metals can be shiny, but Ross pointed out that you get rusty and dull metals. They decide that if you polish a metal it is shiny.

Some metals.

They also noticed that all the non-metals have very different appearances.

a **Look at the photos. What is the difference between the appearance of metals and non-metals?**

oxygen
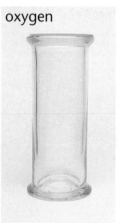

chlorine

bromine

sulphur

Some non-metals.

Solid, liquid or gas?

Most of the elements in the periodic table are solids at room temperature.

b **Look at the diagram of the periodic table.**
   (i) **Are all the metals solids?**
   (ii) **How many elements are gases?**

																	H		He
Li	Be											B	C	N	O	F	Ne
Na	Mg											Al	Si	P	S	Cl	Ar
K	Ca	Sc	Ti	V	Cr	Mn	Fe	Co	Ni	Cu	Zn	Ga	Ge	As	Se	Br	Kr
Rb	Sr	Y	Zr	Nb	Mo	Tc	Ru	Rh	Pd	Ag	Cd	In	Sn	Sb	Te	I	Xe
Cs	Ba	La	Hf	Ta	W	Re	Os	Ir	Pt	Au	Hg	Tl	Pb	Bi	Po	At	Rn
Fr	Ra	Ac															

Key

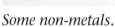 solid ▢ liquid ▢ gas

When you heat a solid metal, it melts and becomes a liquid. Zinc melts at 420°C and gold at 1064°C. These temperatures are their **melting points**.

Bromine is a non-metal that is liquid at room temperature. If you heat it up it boils and becomes a gas. Bromine boils at 59 °C. This temperature is its **boiling point**.

c (i) How many elements are liquid at room temperature?
(ii) Name a non-metal which is solid at room temperature.
(iii) Name a non-metal which is a gas at room temperature.

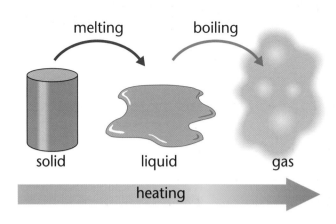

melting   boiling

solid   liquid   gas

heating

Magnetic or not?

Katie says that all metals are **magnetic**, but Ross and Kay disagree. They test lots of elements. They show that only iron, nickel and cobalt are attracted to a magnet. You will learn more about magnetic materials in unit J. Non-metals and most metals are not magnetic.

d Name two metals that are not magnetic.

Chemical reactions

Many elements react in similar ways in chemical reactions. One example of this is when an element reacts with oxygen to make an oxide. Both metals and non-metals react in this way. For example, carbon and oxygen react to make carbon dioxide, and magnesium and oxygen react to make magnesium oxide.

Do you remember?

All metals conduct electricity. They allow electricity to flow easily.

Questions

1 Use the information on these pages to decide if these statements are 'true' or 'false'. Give at least one piece of evidence for each answer.

a All metals are magnetic.   **b** All metals conduct electricity.
c All metals are always shiny.   **d** All metals are solids.

2 Name a non-metal element that is:

a a liquid   **b** a green gas
c a yellow solid   **d** a colourless gas that we need to live.

3 In what three ways are most non-metals different from most metals?

For your notes:

- Elements may be solid, liquid or gas.

- Most metals are solid and shiny when polished. A few metals are magnetic.

- Non-metals are mostly solid or gas. They have many different appearances.

51

Metal or non-metal?

Scientists have used the properties of metals to decide that:

● aluminium, iron, copper, nickel and mercury are metals

● hydrogen, sulphur, bromine and chlorine are non-metals.

Joe's class is thinking about how the scientists decided on these two groups. They want to work out the rules for deciding if an element is a metal or a non-metal. They use the fact files on the opposite page.

Lillian's idea

Put all the solids in one group. Metals are solids. All the others will be non-metals.

Joe's idea

Test the elements with a magnet. Those that stick to the magnet are metals. The others are non-metals.

Yasmin's idea

See which elements conduct electricity. Those that do are metals. Those that don't are non-metals.

a (i) Which elements will be in Lillian's 'metals' group?

(ii) Which elements will be in Lillian's 'non-metals' group?

(iii) Is Lillian's idea going to work? Explain your answer.

b (i) Which elements will be in Joe's 'metals' group?

(ii) Which elements will be in Joe's 'non-metals' group?

(iii) Is Joe's idea going to work? Explain your answer.

c (i) Which elements will be in Yasmin's 'metals' group?

(ii) Which elements will be in Yasmin's 'non-metals' group?

(iii) Is Yasmin's idea going to work? Explain your answer.

What about carbon?

Their teacher then gives them a piece of carbon. The table shows some properties of carbon. Scientists say that carbon is a non-metal.

d Who would say that carbon was a non-metal – Lillian, Joe or Yasmin?

e Think of an idea that will work for carbon and all the elements shown on the opposite page.

Element	Carbon
State at 25 °C	solid
Colour	black
Shiny?	✗
Magnetic?	✗
Conduct electricity?	✓

Fact files

The metals are in red boxes. The non-metals are in yellow boxes.

Element	Copper
Symbol	Cu
State at 25°C	solid
Colour	pink
Shiny?	✓
Magnetic?	✗
Conduct electricity?	✓

Element	Aluminium
Symbol	Al
State at 25°C	solid
Colour	silver
Shiny?	✓
Magnetic?	✗
Conduct electricity?	✓

Element	Iron
Symbol	Fe
State at 25°C	solid
Colour	grey
Shiny?	✓
Magnetic?	✓
Conduct electricity?	✓

Element	Nickel
Symbol	Ni
State at 25°C	solid
Colour	grey
Shiny?	✓
Magnetic?	✓
Conduct electricity?	✓

Element	Mercury
Symbol	Hg
State at 25°C	liquid
Colour	silver
Shiny?	✓
Magnetic?	✗
Conduct electricity?	✓

Element	Hydrogen
Symbol	H
State at 25°C	gas
Colour	colourless
Shiny?	✗
Magnetic?	✗
Conduct electricity?	✗

Element	Sulphur
Symbol	S
State at 25°C	solid
Colour	yellow
Shiny?	✗
Magnetic?	✗
Conduct electricity?	✗

Element	Bromine
Symbol	Br
State at 25°C	liquid
Colour	brown
Shiny?	✗
Magnetic?	✗
Conduct electricity?	✗

Element	Chlorine
Symbol	Cl
State at 25°C	gas
Colour	green
Shiny?	✗
Magnetic?	✗
Conduct electricity?	✗

Questions

1 Selenium is an element.

   a What property of selenium is like a metal?
   b What properties of selenium are like a non-metal?
   c Would you call selenium a metal or a non-metal? Give your reasons.
   d Look back to the periodic table on page 49. Do you agree with the scientists?

Element	Selenium
State at 25°C	solid
Colour	silver
Shiny?	✓
Magnetic?	✗
Conduct electricity?	✗

E5 Reacting elements

Burning elements

Kay's class is burning elements. The teacher burns magnesium and it reacts with oxygen. She asks the class to decide if a new substance is made.

ⓐ Do you think a chemical reaction has taken place? Give reasons for your answer.

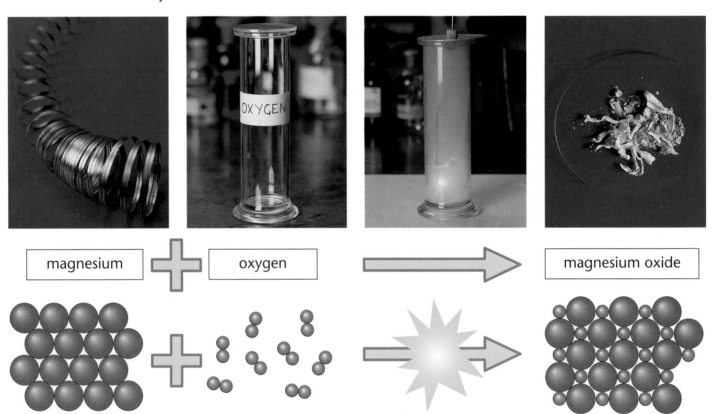

New substances

When magnesium burns in oxygen an oxide is made. It is a new substance called magnesium oxide. Magnesium oxide is not an element. It is made up of more than one type of atom. It is a **compound**. Elements react together to make compounds.

Look at the diagram above of the particles in magnesium oxide. There are magnesium atoms and oxygen atoms. Each magnesium atom is next to oxygen atoms. Each oxygen atom is next to magnesium atoms. They joined together during the chemical reaction.

ⓑ Which two elements reacted together to make the new compound?

ⓒ What is the name of the new compound?

Every compound has a formula

It would take too long to draw particle diagrams every time we want to show the atoms in compounds. We can use symbols to represent the atoms. We show magnesium oxide by writing **MgO**. This shows that there are magnesium atoms and oxygen atoms in the compound. It also reminds us that magnesium oxide is not an element. MgO is a formula. Each compound has a **formula**.

d CuO is the formula for a compound.
  (i) Which two types of atom does this compound contain?
  (ii) Name the compound. (*Hint:* Look back to page 48 if you can't remember what Cu stands for.)

Predicting how elements react

We have already seen that when elements burn in oxygen, they react to make oxides. Elements that react with sulphur all react in a similar way to make sulphides.

Hydrogen reacts with sulphur to make hydrogen sulphide. The hydrogen and sulphur atoms react and join together. Hydrogen sulphide is a compound.

hydrogen + sulphur → hydrogen sulphide

element + element → compound

e Magnesium and sulphur react in a similar way. Copy and complete the word equation.

magnesium + sulphur → _____ _____

Questions

1 Match the beginnings and ends to make sentences.

Beginning	End
Elements contain …	… more than one type of atom joined together.
Compounds contain …	… elements react together.
Compounds are made when …	… only one type of atom.

2 Copy and complete these two word equations.

  a zinc + oxygen → _____ _____
  b calcium + oxygen → _____ _____

3 Match the names and the formulas for these compounds.

Name	Formula
iron oxide	ZnO
carbon monoxide	FeO
zinc oxide	CO

Did you know?

The pictures of atoms on these pages are 25 million times bigger than the real atoms.

For your notes:

- Elements react together to make **compounds**.

- A **compound** is a substance with more than one type of atom joined together.

- Each compound has a **formula**.

F1 Compounds all around

Learn about:
- The range of compounds
- The properties of compounds

Elements and compounds

In Unit E Atoms and elements you learnt that an element is a substance that contains only one type of atom and a compound is a substance with more than one type of atom joined together.

Is it water?

Water is a compound. The diagram on the right shows two molecules. The molecule on the left is a water molecule. The molecule contains two hydrogen atoms and one oxygen atom. The white balls stand for hydrogen and the red ball stands for oxygen.

ⓐ **How many different atoms are there in water?**

ⓑ **Why isn't water an element?**

The molecule on the right in the diagram is a **hydrogen peroxide** molecule. Hydrogen peroxide is also a compound. It also contains hydrogen and oxygen atoms joined together.

ⓒ **What is the difference between the water molecule and the hydrogen peroxide molecule?**

Do you remember?

A molecule is a group of atoms joined together. They can be the same atom, as in an oxygen molecule, or they can be a group of different types of atoms, like in carbon dioxide.

Did you know?

One extra oxygen atom makes a big difference. Hydrogen peroxide is a dangerous, corrosive liquid. Diluted with water it is used as a disinfectant.

Fisher Chemicals
Hydrogen peroxide 20 volumes
Hydrogène peroxide >6% en poids (20 volume)
Wasserstoffperoxid >6% w/v
Waterstofperoxide >6%

Ⓕ Fisher Scientific

Sodium chloride

The photo on the left shows some salt crystals. The scientific name for salt is sodium chloride. Each sodium chloride crystal contains millions of atoms. The diagram below shows a model of sodium chloride. The grey balls stand for the sodium atoms and the green balls stand for the chlorine atoms. You can see how the atoms are arranged in a pattern.

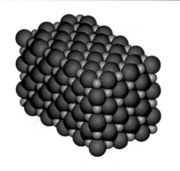

ⓓ **Look at the diagram of the model. How do we know that sodium chloride is a compound?**

ⓔ **What is the everyday name for sodium chloride?**

Sodium chloride has the formula NaCl. This shows:

- it contains sodium atoms and chlorine atoms
- there is one sodium atom for every one chlorine atom.

Sodium is a shiny, silver metal. It is corrosive and flammable in air.

Chlorine is a poisonous green gas.

Melting points

Sodium chloride, sodium and chlorine have different melting points. The melting point is the temperature at which a solid melts. Sodium chloride has a melting point of 801 °C. This is much higher than the melting point of sodium (98 °C) or chlorine (–101 °C).

Each **pure** substance has a known melting point and boiling point. You can look them up in a book or on the Internet.

Hazard to harmless

The compound sodium chloride is very different from the two elements called sodium and chlorine.

Sodium chloride is a solid with colourless crystals.

f **Sodium and chlorine are both dangerous to handle. How do you know that sodium chloride is safe?**

Questions

1 Copy and complete these sentences by pairing up the correct beginnings and ends.

Beginnings	Ends
Compounds are shown by ...	... symbols.
All pure substances have known ...	... formulae.
Elements are shown by ...	... from the elements that made them.
Compounds have different properties ...	... melting points and boiling points.

2 Copy and complete the table below using the information on these two pages.

Substance	Sodium	Chlorine	Sodium chloride
Element or compund?			
Symbol or formula	Na	Cl	
Solid, liquid or gas?			
Colour			
Melting point in °C			

For your notes:

- Some compounds contain molecules.

- Other compounds have different types of atoms fixed together to make crystals.

- Compounds are very different from the elements that made them.

- All **pure** substances have a known melting point and a known boiling point.

F2 Reacting compounds

In a flash

Kevin's class is looking at reactions involving compounds. His teacher, Mrs McMichaels, shows them a reaction shown in this photo between copper oxide, a compound, and zinc, an element.

a How do you know that a chemical reaction had taken place?

The word equation for the reaction is:

zinc + copper oxide → copper + zinc oxide

One compound, copper oxide, has reacted to make another compound, zinc oxide.

b What are: (i) the reactants?
(ii) the products of this reaction?

There was bright flame and lots of smoke.

Look at the diagram on the right showing the particles in copper oxide. Compare it to the diagram on the far right showing the particles in zinc oxide.

● copper ● oxygen

● zinc ● oxygen

c How are copper oxide and zinc oxide different?

d Where did the zinc atoms come from to make the zinc oxide?

e Where did the copper atoms go to when the copper oxide reacted?

A yellow solid has been made.

All change

Kevin and Bianca then carry out a second reaction. They take some sodium iodide and dissolve it in water. It makes a colourless solution. They then take some lead nitrate and dissolve that in water. It makes another colourless solution.

Then they mix the two solutions. This is shown in the photo on the left.

f What *two* observations show that a chemical reaction has taken place?

The reactants are sodium iodide and lead nitrate. The products are lead iodide and sodium nitrate. The lead iodide is the yellow solid. The lead iodide is a **precipitate**. A precipitate is a solid that is made when two liquids react.

g Write a word equation for this reaction.

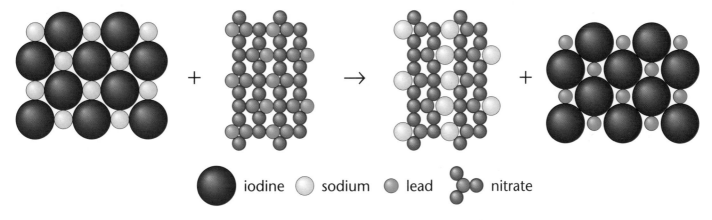

○ iodine ○ sodium ○ lead ⚛ nitrate

h Where did: (i) the lead atoms and
(ii) the iodine atoms come from to make the lead iodide?

Bubble

Chemical reactions also happen in cells. Look at the photo on the right. The pea is in a solution of hydrogen peroxide. The cells change the hydrogen peroxide into water and oxygen.

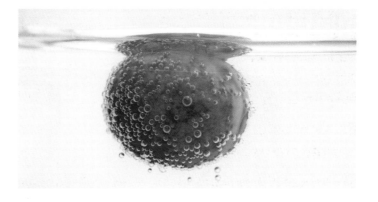

i What evidence, shown in this photo, shows that a chemical reaction is taking place?

Questions

1 Copy and complete these word equations. Use the information on these two pages to help you.

   a zinc + copper oxide → _____ + _____
   b hydrogen peroxide + _____ → water + _____

2 Which reaction described on these two pages showed:

   a a colour change?
   b energy given out?
   c bubbles being made?
   d a precipitate?

For your notes:

● Compounds change into other compounds, or make elements, in chemical reactions.

● A **precipitate** is a solid made when two liquids react.

F3 What's in it?

Water, water everywhere

Bianca, Ellie and Kevin are investigating water. They collect samples of different types of water. They have been asked to find out if the water is **pure**.

Do you remember?

Pure means there is only one substance present. Pure water contains water only.

Using the label

They start by investigating the mineral water, because it has a label.

a Look at the label. Name three substances the mineral water contains other than water.

NATURAL MINERAL WATER

1.5 LITRE e

TYPICAL ANALYSIS mg/L:

Ca	35.0	HCO$_3$	136.0	F	<0.1
Mg	8.5	Cl	7.5	Fe	<0.01
Na	6.0	SO$_4$	6.0	Al	<0.01
K	0.6	NO$_3$	<0.1	T.D.S at 100°C	136

CALORIE FREE   pH at source 7.8
LOW MINERAL CONTENT.
SUITABLE FOR A LOW SODIUM DIET.
ONCE OPENED STORE IN REFRIGERATOR
AND USE WITHIN 7 DAYS.

What's left?

*The mineral water is not pure. It is a **mixture**. Look at all the other stuff it contains.*

We know that the seawater is a mixture. Seawater tastes salty.

Let's evaporate the water from the seawater and see if there is anything left when the water has gone.

Do you remember?

Filtration, evaporation, distillation and chromatography are all ways of separating mixtures.

b Predict what will be left when the water is evaporated from the seawater.

When all the water is evaporated they are left with a white, powdery solid shown in the photo on the right. This is a **mixture** of sodium chloride (salt) and other substances.

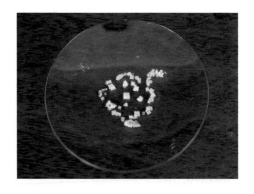

Distilled

Ellie asks Mrs Cook, the science technician, how the distilled water is made. Mrs Cook explains that it is made from tap water by distillation. The tap water is heated until it boils. The water turns into steam, leaving any other substances behind. The steam is collected and condensed.

c How is the tap water distilled?

d Do you think the distilled water is pure?
Explain your answer.

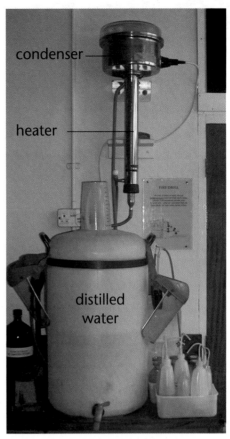

Apparatus for distilling water.

Other mixtures

Most of the materials around us are mixtures. Petrol, washing powder, paint and paper are all mixtures. That is why we can have different types of petrol, different washing powders, different coloured paint and different types of paper.

If a substance is a compound, you know exactly what is in it. Think again about water. Pure water only contains water molecules. The diagram on the right shows that each water molecule contains two hydrogen atoms and one oxygen atom.

The mineral water contains lots of different substances. Different types of mineral water contain different substances.

Mixtures vary, compounds are always the same.

Questions

1 Look at these diagrams showing the particles in six different gases.

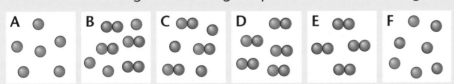

a Which gases are pure? **b** Which gases are mixtures?
c Which gases are elements? **d** Which gases are compounds?

2 Decide if these statements are *true* or *false*.

a Mixtures contain only one substance.
b A pure element is a mixture. **d** Mixtures vary.
c A pure compound is a mixture. **e** Compounds vary.

For your notes:

- **Mixtures** contain more than one substance.

- Pure substances contain only one element or one compound.

- Mixtures vary. Compounds are always the same.

The air around us

What's in air?

Air is a mixture of nitrogen, oxygen and other gases. The particles in air are shown in the top diagram. The different substances in air are shown in the pie chart. The air contains mostly nitrogen and oxygen molecules.

The substances in air can vary. Air near a bonfire contains smoke. Air in a garden contains scent made by flowers. The amount of each substance in air can also vary. The air in a crowded lift contains less oxygen than in an empty lift, because the people will be taking oxygen out of the air.

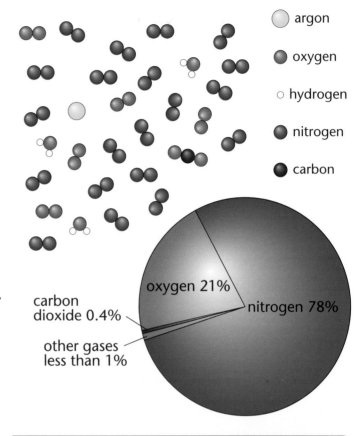

argon
oxygen
hydrogen
nitrogen
carbon

oxygen 21%
carbon dioxide 0.4%
other gases less than 1%
nitrogen 78%

a Use the pie chart to answer these questions.
   (i) Which gas makes up most of the air?
   (ii) Which gas makes up 21% of the air?

b Use the diagram to answer these questions. Which particles in air are:
   (i) molecules?   (ii) single atoms?

Pure or mixture?

Mrs McMichaels asks her class: "Find out how a scientist could tell the difference between air and nitrogen."

Kevin finds out that pure substances boil at one temperature, the boiling point.

Ellie looks up the boiling point of nitrogen. It is −196 °C.

Then they think about what would happen with the air. The air contains mostly nitrogen and oxygen. The boiling point of oxygen is −183 °C. They imagine the scientist cooling the air.

Do you remember?

When you heat a solid it melts and becomes a liquid, then boils and becomes a gas. When you cool a gas it condenses to make a liquid, then freezes to make a solid.

The air is a mixture. The nitrogen is a pure substance.

If the scientist cooled the nitrogen gas, it would condense at −196 °C.

Water boils and condenses at 100 °C. What temperature does nitrogen boil and condense at?

When you cool a gas it will condense into a liquid. So, when you cool the air the oxygen would condense at −183 °C. Then the nitrogen would condense at −196 °C.

c Which gas would all condense at one temperature, air or nitrogen?

Separating air

We need pure oxygen for use in hospitals. Oxygen is added to the air to make it easier for some patients to breathe.

Pure oxygen is made from air. The air is cooled to −200 °C. This means all the nitrogen and all the oxygen will have condensed. It will be liquid air.

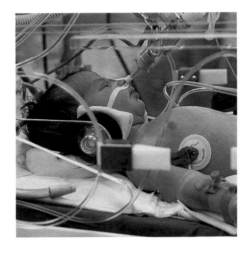
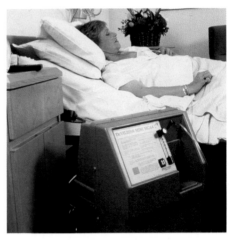

The liquid air is then heated up. The nitrogen boils first at −196 °C. The nitrogen all boils away. The oxygen boils next, at −183 °C, making oxygen gas. The machine in the far right photo concentrates oxygen from the air to treat the patient.

d What temperature does nitrogen boil at?

e What temperature does oxygen boil at?

Questions

1 Copy and complete these two sentences by pairing up the correct beginnings and ends.

Beginnings

Mixtures do not have …
Pure substances have …

Ends

… only one substance present.
… one boiling point or one melting point.

2 Lesley and Clare find out about a different way of telling air and nitrogen apart. They find out about a 'gas chromatography' machine. This separates the gases in the mixture, like chromatography uses paper to separate coloured dyes.

This diagram shows the results of putting two gases through the 'gas chromatography' machine.

a Which gas is nitrogen and which is air?
b Explain how you came to your decision.

For your notes:

- Pure substances melt and freeze at one temperature, the melting point.

- Pure substances boil and condense at one temperature, the boiling point.

- Mixtures change state over a range of temperatures.

F5 Formulae

Ratios

Scientists use **ratios** to work out the formulae for compounds.

Look at the diagram on the right. It shows the compound sodium chloride. There are 25 atoms of sodium and 25 atoms of chlorine. We work out the *ratio* like this:

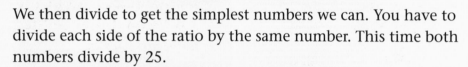

number of sodium atoms : number of chlorine atoms
25 : 25

We then divide to get the simplest numbers we can. You have to divide each side of the ratio by the same number. This time both numbers divide by 25.

$25 \div 25 : 25 \div 25$
1 : 1

The *ratio* of sodium atoms to chlorine atoms is 1:1. There is one sodium atom for each chlorine atom. This is why the formula for sodium chloride is NaCl.

chlorine   sodium

Look at the diagram on the right. It shows the compound calcium chloride. There are 12 atoms of calcium and 24 atoms of chlorine.

calcium : chloride
12 : 24

This time both numbers divide by 12.

$12 \div 12 : 24 \div 12$
1 : 2

The ratio of calcium atoms to chlorine atoms is 1:2. This is why the formula for calcium chloride is $CaCl_2$.

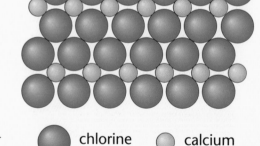

chlorine   calcium

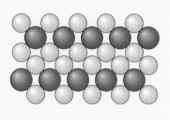

oxygen   sodium

Look at the diagram on the left. It shows the compound sodium oxide. There are 20 atoms of sodium and 10 atoms of oxygen.

sodium : oxygen
20 : 10
2 : 1

The ratio of sodium to oxygen atoms is 2:1. This is why the formula for sodium oxide is Na_2O.

Work out the formula

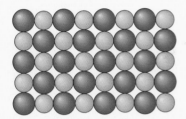

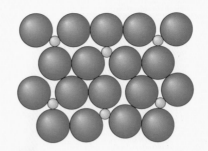

○ calcium ● oxygen

● chlorine ○ aluminium

● nitrogen ○ sodium

ⓐ Check that the formula for calcium oxide is CaO. Count the atoms, then work out the ratio. Copy the box below, filling in the question marks.

ⓑ Work out the formula for aluminium chloride. Copy the box below, filling in the question marks.

ⓒ Work out the formula for sodium nitride. Copy the box below, filling in the question marks.

calcium : oxygen
? : ?
? : ?
The formula is CaO

aluminium : chlorine
? : ?
? : ?
The formula is $AlCl_?$

sodium : nitrogen
? : ?
? : ?
The formula is $Na_?N$

Working out the number of atoms

The formula for sodium chloride is NaCl. This means the ratio of sodium atoms to chlorine atoms in 1:1. If there is one sodium atom, there is one chlorine atom. If there are 100 sodium atoms, there are 100 chlorine atoms.

ⓓ There are 200 sodium atoms. How many chlorine atoms are there?

ⓔ There are one million chlorine atoms. How many sodium atoms are there?

ⓕ The formula for aluminium chloride is $AlCl_3$. There are one billion aluminium atoms. How many atoms of chlorine are there?

ⓖ The formula for sodium oxide is Na_2O. There are four trillion sodium atoms. How many oxygen atoms are there?

Questions

1 Draw diagrams of these solids showing how the atoms may be arranged.

  a MgO   **b** $MgCl_2$.

2 Some compounds contain molecules. Water is a compound that contains molecules. It has the formula H_2O. A molecule of water is shown on the right.

Suggest and draw molecules for compounds with these formulae. Use different colours for the different types of atoms in the molecules.

  a SO_2 **b** CH_4 **c** C_2H_6 **d** N_2O.

G1 Rock breaking

What are rocks?

Rocks are everywhere. We walk on them and build with them. There are many types of rock. Some are made of **grains**. Some are made of **crystals**.

The grains and crystals are made of compounds called **minerals**. Different rocks are made up of different minerals or different mixtures of minerals.

a What is a mineral?

A close fit?

The way the grains or crystals fit together gives the rocks their **texture**.

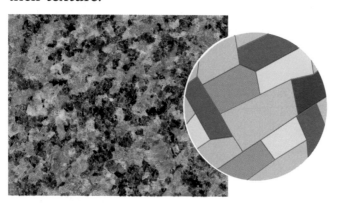

Look at the photo of **granite** above. It is made of crystals which fit together with no gaps between them. We say they are **interlocking**.

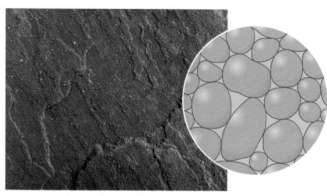

Look at the photo of **sandstone** above. It is made of grains which do not fit together. There are gaps between them because they have a round shape. They are **non-interlocking**.

What happens if you drop water onto the surface of a rock? It stays on the surface of some rocks, but with others it soaks into them. Rocks with non-interlocking grains are often **porous**. Water can get into the gaps between the grains and soak in.

b Granite has interlocking crystals. What will happen if you drop water onto granite?

Weathering

All rocks gradually get broken down into smaller pieces where they are. We call this **weathering**.

In the photo on the right, the small rocks at the bottom of the slope used to be part of the mountain. They broke off the mountain and fell to the ground.

When rock is broken into smaller pieces, but not changed into different substances, we call it **physical weathering**. This can be caused by frost and changes in temperature.

Water and ice

In the mountains, there is often a lot of water which freezes and thaws again many times. The diagrams on the right show what happens when water gets into small cracks or holes in a rock.

C What happens to water as it freezes?

Hot and cold

In a desert, it is very hot during the day, but it can get very cold at night. During the day, the hot rocks expand. During the cold nights, they contract.

This happens every day and night, causing cracks to appear in the rock. The rock breaks apart into smaller pieces. These are broken down into small grains of sand.

1 Water gets into cracks in the rock.

2 The water freezes and it expands.

3 The force of the ice makes the crack bigger.

4 The crack gets so big that part of the rock breaks off.

expansion

contraction

stresses in the rock cause it to crack

d What happens to rocks when they get hot?

e What happens to rocks when they get cold?

For your notes:

- Rocks are made up of **grains** or **crystals**. These are made of different compounds called **minerals**.

- **Physical weathering** happens when rocks are broken down into smaller pieces but not changed into different substances.

- Physical weathering is caused by frost and changes in temperature.

Questions

1 Look at diagrams A and B.

A   B

a Which one shows interlocking crystals?
b Which one could be a porous rock?

2 Copy and complete these sentences.

When rock is broken into smaller pieces, but not changed into different _____, we call this _____ weathering. It can be caused by _____ and changes in _____.

G2 Disappearing rocks

Acid on the rocks

Many statues and buildings are made of a rock called **limestone**. Limestone is weathered easily by rainwater. Rainwater is a slightly acidic solution. This is because it contains carbon dioxide from the air dissolved in it.

A limestone statue.

The photo above shows some rainwater being tested using a pH probe. The probe shows the pH of the water.

ⓐ **Is the water acidic or alkaline?**

ⓑ **Why is the pH probe more precise than using universal indicator paper?**

When rainwater falls on rocks, it can get into any cracks or into gaps between grains.

Limestone is made of calcium carbonate. When acid reacts with calcium carbonate a new substance is made which is soluble in water. Carbon dioxide is also made. Over thousands of years, holes and cracks begin to appear, as shown in this photo of limestone pavement at Malham Cove in Yorkshire.

Weathering, when chemical changes take place in the rock, is called **chemical weathering**. Chemicals in the rainwater react with minerals in the rock and form new substances. In the photo on page 69, chemical weathering has changed the colour of the stone.

c **What is chemical weathering?**

Granite is different. Granite is weathered more slowly than limestone. Only some of the minerals in the rock react with acidic water to make new substances. This gradually weakens the rock, causing it to crumble and change.

d **Why does chemical weathering change granite more slowly than limestone?**

Soil

When rock is chemically and physically weathered, it turns into soil. The top layer of soil is called **topsoil**. This contains tiny grains of sand and clay. Larger pieces of rock in the soil are stones. Topsoil also contains decayed plant and animal matter called humus. **Humus** is rich in minerals that plants need for growth.

e **What is humus?**

topsoil (with humus)

subsoil (no humus)

broken rock

solid rock

Questions

1 Copy and complete these sentences by choosing from the words below.

chemicals   sand   weathering   acid

changes   substances   wind

Chemical _____ can be caused by _____ in rainwater.
Chemical _____ take place in the rocks and new _____ are made.

2 A gravestone from 1780 is very difficult to read. The letters on a gravestone from 1945 are much clearer. Explain why you think this might be.

3 Explain why a designer might suggest building a new town hall from granite.

For your notes:

- Rainwater becomes acidic when carbon dioxide is dissolved in it.

- **Chemical weathering** is caused by reactions between acidic water and minerals in the rock.

- Soil forms when rocks are weathered.

G3 Transporting rock

Where did it go?

When this house was built, it was a long way from the edge of the cliff. Over the years the rock has collapsed into the sea. Finally, the edge of the cliff is so close that the house is in danger of collapsing too.

a **Explain why the house is falling into the sea.**

The weathered pieces of rock from the cliff are carried away by the waves and currents in the sea. As they are carried, the rocks knock against each other and bits break off. The pieces become more rounded and smaller. The broken pieces of rock wear away the solid rocks of the cliff when waves crash against it. These processes are called **erosion**. Erosion can be caused by moving water or the wind.

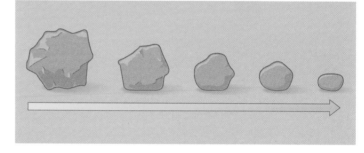

Water

Rivers can carry away large amounts of weathered rock from mountains and hills. Rivers move very fast near to their source in the mountain. Here the water can carry quite large pieces of rock. Rivers move more slowly when they get close to the sea. Here they can only carry small grains of rock.

b **Which will be able to carry larger rock pieces, a mountain stream or a large river near the sea? Explain your answer.**

Wind

The wind can only carry small, light grains of sand. It cannot carry large pieces of rock because they are too heavy. If the wind is strong it may be able to carry slightly larger grains of sand, as in the desert sandstorm shown in this photo.

c Why do you think a strong wind can carry bigger grains of sand than a gentle breeze?

Deposition

As a river slows down, it can no longer carry along large pieces of rock. They settle to the bottom of the river. This is called **deposition**. The bits that settle out are called **sediment**. Grains of similar sizes are deposited together. When the river is travelling very slowly, it can only carry very fine grains.

Finally, the slow-moving river flows into the sea. Layers of sediment are deposited here. These build up to form new land and the river runs over it in lots of small streams. This is called a **delta**.

d Why do you get a lot of fine sediment where a river flows into the sea, but not near its source?

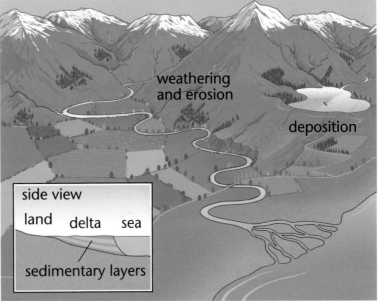

weathering and erosion

deposition

side view

land   delta   sea

sedimentary layers

Questions

1 Copy and complete these sentences by choosing from the words below.

bigger   deposited   carried away   slow   water   wind

Erosion happens when weathered rock is _____. Rock can be eroded by _____ or _____. Fast-moving wind and water can carry _____ pieces than _____-moving wind or water. When the wind or water is no longer moving fast enough to carry the rock pieces, they are _____.

2 After heavy rain, water runs off the fields into rivers. Explain why a river in flood looks dirty.

3 You are a lump of rock next to the river on the side of a mountain. You are hit by a large stone and washed into the river. Describe your journey to the sea.

For your notes:

- **Erosion** happens when rock is carried away from where it was weathered. It makes the rock pieces rounded and smaller.

- Rock can be eroded by wind or water.

- Fast-moving wind and water can carry larger pieces of rock than slow-moving wind or water.

- **Deposition** happens when pieces of rock that were carried settle on to the Earth's surface again.

71

What happens to the sediment?

The sediments carried by rivers are deposited at the bottom of lakes or seas. Over millions of years the layers of sediment build up. These are called **sedimentary layers**.

The sediment is in layers. This is because the rivers carry different sized grains. There are clear boundaries between the layers. This is because there are times when the rivers carry hardly any sediment and times when they carry a lot.

The picture on the right shows how layers form when you shake up gravel, sand and clay with water and then leave them to settle.

a Which layer contains:
  (i) the smallest pieces?
  (ii) the largest pieces?

dirty water

mud and clay

sand

pebbles

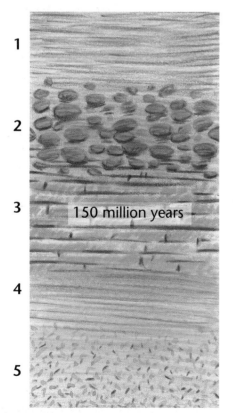

1

2

3   150 million years

4

5

What are fossils?

Any parts of creatures that are preserved in sedimentary layers are called **fossils**. Fossils are very important because they can tell us about organisms that lived millions of years ago when the layers were deposited. Much of our knowledge of the Earth's past comes from fossils.

b What is a fossil?

Rock history

When you look at sedimentary layers, the oldest layers are at the bottom because they were deposited first. Different layers are made of different sediments.

c Look at the diagram on the left. Is layer 2 of rounded stones older or younger than the blue brick-like layer 3?

Look at this photo of the Grand Canyon in Arizona, USA. It was carved out by a river. The layers near the top of the canyon are 100 million years old. At the very bottom they are even older, almost one billion years old.

Imagine we find a fossil of an animal that we know only lived between 100 and 110 million years ago. This tells us that the sediment layer that the fossil was found in is between 100 and 110 million years old.

This sort of information helps us to find out what was happening on Earth at different times in the past.

People who study rocks are called **geologists**. They are like Earth detectives. Fossils are very useful to them.

Questions

1 Copy and complete these sentences by choosing from the words below.

     fossils   **layers**   **sediment**   **water**

Sedimentary layers are made from _____. They build up in _____ over millions of years at the bottom of lakes or seas. Parts of creatures that are preserved in sedimentary layers are called _____.

2 Answer the following questions using the diagram of rock layers on page 72.

  a Which layer of rock is the oldest?
  b Which layer of rock is the youngest?
  c Which layers are older than 150 million years old?

3 Make up a poem about being an Earth detective using the words below.

     fossils   **rock**   **dig**

d A rock contains a fossil of an animal that lived between 70 and 85 million years ago. What is the oldest age that the rock could be?

For your notes:

- Sediments settle at the bottom of lakes or on the sea bed in **sedimentary layers**.

- Any parts of creatures that are preserved in sedimentary layers are called **fossils**. Fossils are very important because they are a way of finding out how old the rock is.

G5 Earth detectives

The fossil finder

Many people think Mary Anning was the greatest fossil hunter ever. She was born in Lyme Regis, Dorset in 1799. When she was 11, her father died. This left the family very poor.

To make money for her family, Mary began to collect fossils from the local beach. She sold them to wealthy collectors and museums. Fossil hunting was dangerous. She had to walk and wade under crumbling cliffs at low tide.

Mary became well known as a fossil hunter and she made some very important discoveries. She found the first specimen of an *Ichthyosaurus* in 1821 and the first nearly complete skeleton of a *Plesiosaurus* in 1823.

Mary Anning.

Ichthyosaurus.

Plesiosaurus.

Fossils can explain events that happened on the Earth thousands or millions of years ago. They can tell us how life on Earth has changed.

ⓐ **Why do people look for fossils?**

A fishy story

Mike and Michelle are geologists in their spare time. They were on holiday in Lyme Regis. Each day they hunted for fossils on the beach. One day, Mike was chipping away at a piece of rock from the cliff face when he found an unusual fossil. It appeared to be the fossil of a fish that lived 190 million years ago. They were both puzzled about how it got there.

ⓑ **Why was Mike surprised?**

This is unusual, this fossil looks like a fish that lived 190 million years ago. But it can't be because dead fish sink to the sea bed, not jump into cliff faces.

Solving the problem

Mike decided to think about the problem in different ways.

Something tells me that fossil must have got there because the Earth has changed …

Mike had a gut reaction.
He was thinking intuitively.

I must read about fossils in my Beginner's Guide to Geology.

Mike was checking the facts. He was thinking neutrally.

We should find out if there are any more of these fossils and make a note of where they are found.

Mike was making notes to help others. He was thinking constructively.

Perhaps I should decide which of my ideas to follow.

Mike was thinking about his thinking. He was reflecting.

I mustn't rush into saying I have found something new – I might be mistaken.

Mike was thinking about the risks. He was thinking cautiously.

Lateral thinking

Sometimes things we see do not fit in with what we already know. We need to think of new ideas and look at other scientific facts. This is called **lateral thinking**. Lateral means sideways, so thinking laterally means thinking in a different direction.

Michelle suddenly had a flash of inspiration.

C **What new scientific fact did Michelle take into account?**

You are right, the oldest fossils are found in the deepest rocks, but Earth movements or earthquakes can push rocks up. Maybe Earth movements have raised up the rocks, together with any fossils in them.

Questions

1 How many different types of thinking did Mike and Michelle use to solve the problem?

2 Which type of thinking explained how the fossil of the fish that lived 190 million years ago got up into the cliff face?

3 Imagine you found a fossil of a dinosaur bone on the beach. Explain how you think it could have got there.

H1 Hard rocks

Learn about:
● Sedimentary rocks
● Metamorphic rocks

Rock solid

Grains from weathered and eroded rocks build up in sedimentary layers. Over millions of years these sedimentary layers gradually turn to **sedimentary rocks**. The rocks sometimes contain fossils from dead remains of creatures in the sedimentary layers.

How do the grains turn to solid rock? As the sediment builds up, there is an enormous weight pressing on the lower layers. The grains become pressed tightly together. This is called **compaction**. Between the grains are tiny gaps that contain water.

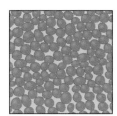

Sedimentary rock is a bit like a sandwich: built up in layers.

In the lake or sea where sediments are deposited, there are chemicals dissolved in the water. The compaction squeezes out most of the water from the tiny gaps between the grains. The chemicals in the water crystallise in the gaps between the grains. They 'glue' the grains together. This is called **cementation**.

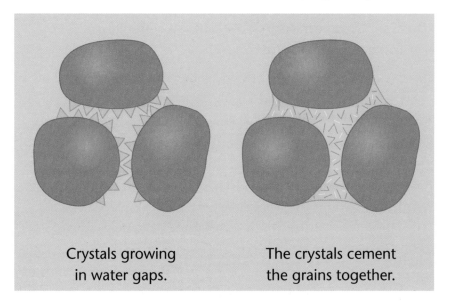

Crystals growing in water gaps.

The crystals cement the grains together.

a How are the grains in sedimentary rock stuck together?

Types of sedimentary rock

There are many types of sedimentary rock, made from different minerals.

Limestone is mostly made from the shells and bones of small sea animals. Millions of years ago there were warm shallow seas full of sea animals. Their dead bodies were deposited on the sea bed. The calcium carbonate in the rock comes from their shells and bones.

Do you remember?

Limestone is made of calcium carbonate. When you add acid to calcium carbonate, it fizzes and gives off carbon dioxide.

Limestone occurs in different colours. This is because different compounds mix with the calcium carbonate. Yellow or brown limestones get their colour from iron compounds.

ⓑ Which gas is made when you add acid to limestone?

These rocks (left and right) are limestones.

Sandstone is made from grains of sand cemented together. Both limestone and sandstone are used as building materials.

Changing rocks

When sedimentary rocks are buried deeper in the Earth, they become squeezed or heated up, or both. The minerals in the rock change chemically without the rocks actually melting. New minerals form as crystals. The new rock is called **metamorphic rock**.

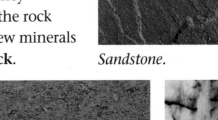

Sandstone.

In metamorphic rocks, the crystals are interlocking so the rock is not porous. Metamorphic rocks do not usually have fossils because the fossils are destroyed when the rock changes.

ⓒ How do sedimentary rocks change to metamorphic rocks?

ⓓ Look at the photos on the right. Describe the differences between limestone and marble.

*Limestone (left) is changed into **marble** (right) by heat and increased pressure.*

Questions

1 Copy and complete these sentences by choosing from the words below.

> **compaction   cementation   sedimentation**
> **metamorphic   sedimentary**

Sedimentary layers are made from grains of rock and the dead remains of sea creatures. The grains are pressed tightly together and the water is squeezed out. This is called _____. The chemicals in the water make crystals between the sediments, 'gluing' them together. This is called _____. The sediment turns to _____ rock.

2 Limestone is mainly calcium carbonate, which is white. Why do we find different coloured limestones?

3 Describe the differences between a sedimentary rock and a metamorphic rock.

For your notes:

- **Sedimentary rocks** are made from layers of sediment. The pressure of the layers causes **compaction** and **cementation** of the grains.

- **Limestone** and **sandstone** are sedimentary rocks.

- **Metamorphic rocks** are made when heat or high pressure, or both, changes existing rocks.

- **Marble** is a metamorphic rock.

Igneous rocks

As well as sedimentary and metamorphic rocks, there is a third type of rock called **igneous rock**.

Igneous rocks are made from liquid or molten rock called **magma**. Magma comes from inside the Earth where it is very hot. The magma rises up to the crust of the Earth.

When the magma reaches the surface of the Earth it is called **lava**. Sometimes the magma is forced out and erupts from a volcano, as shown in the photo on the right. Magma might also be blown out as volcanic ash.

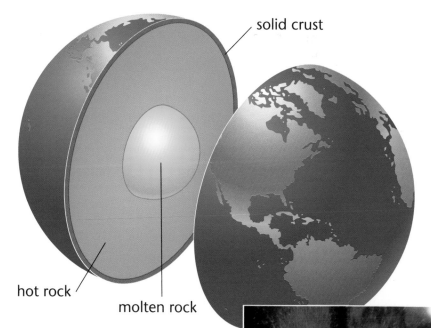

solid crust

hot rock

molten rock

A slice through the Earth.

Types of igneous rock

At the surface, the lava cools quickly and forms igneous rock with small crystals. **Basalt** is an example of this sort of igneous rock.

Sometimes the magma never reaches the surface but cools slowly underground. This forms igneous rock with large crystals. **Granite** is an example of this type of igneous rock.

Molten rock cooling quickly forms basalt.

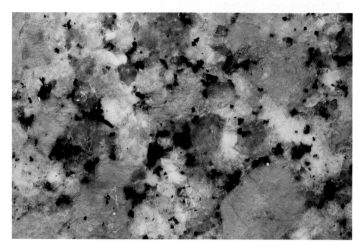

Molten rock cooling more slowly forms granite.

a Describe where granite and basalt are formed in a volcano.

Fast and slow cooling

Class 8T imagined that they were particles in molten rock. They moved around the classroom shaking hands as often as possible with each other. When the teacher said 'Start cooling', they stuck together in groups.

b (i) **What do you think would happen to the size of the groups if the cooling time became longer?**

    (ii) **How does this activity show that slow cooling gives larger crystals?**

Differences between igneous rocks

Different types of igneous rock have different colours because they contain different minerals. We can classify igneous rocks into two groups. The lighter coloured rocks contain minerals which are rich in silica, but not much iron. The darker coloured rocks contain less silica but a lot of iron-rich minerals.

c Which minerals give a dark colour to igneous rocks?

d Look at the photos on page 78 of granite and basalt. Which rock contains more iron-rich minerals?

Questions

1 Copy and complete these sentences using the words below.

    large   lava   quickly   slowly   small   volcano

When the magma reaches the surface it is called _____. Sometimes the magma is forced out and erupts from a _____. At the surface, the lava cools _____ and forms igneous rock with _____ crystals. Sometimes the magma never reaches the surface but cools _____ underground. This forms igneous rock with _____ crystals

2 How can you tell the difference between granite and basalt? Explain why they are different.

3 Rhyolite is a pale pink rock which comes from a volcano. Use the information on these two pages to predict two other properties of rhyolite.

For your notes:

- **Igneous rocks** are made from liquid or molten rock called **magma**.

- Igneous rocks with small crystals cooled quickly at the Earth's surface. Igneous rocks with large crystals cooled slowly underground.

- Igneous rocks contain different minerals. This gives them different colours.

H3 Rock on

The rock cycle

Rocks in one of the three main groups may change into another group over millions of years. This is called the **rock cycle**, and is shown in the diagram below.

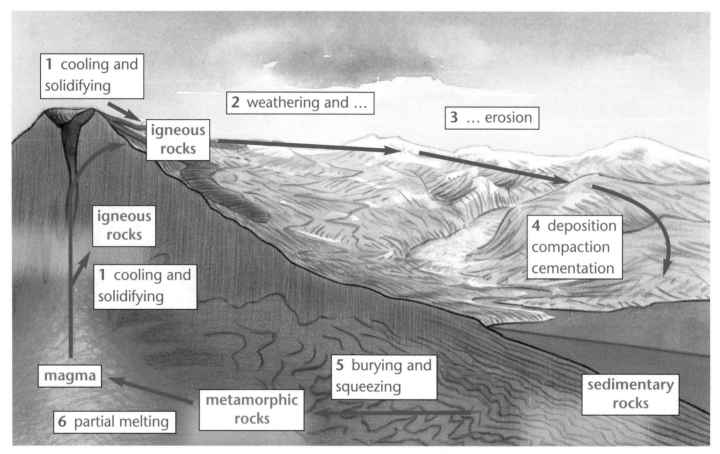

1 **cooling and solidifying**

2 **weathering and …**

3 **… erosion**

igneous rocks

igneous rocks

1 **cooling and solidifying**

4 **deposition compaction cementation**

magma

5 **burying and squeezing**

6 **partial melting**

metamorphic rocks

sedimentary rocks

1 Igneous rocks are formed when magma cools and solidifies.

2 These rocks are worn away by weathering on the Earth's surface.

3 The weathered rocks are transported away by rivers and wind and eroded.

4 Rock fragments are deposited as sediment on the sea bed to make sedimentary rocks.

5 Some sedimentary rocks are changed by heat and pressure into metamorphic rocks.

6 Some metamorphic rocks partly melt and produce magma.

a Name the three main groups rocks can be divided into.

b Look at the diagram of the rock cycle. How many different processes are involved?

Which type?

The properties of the rocks you have met in this unit are summarised in the table opposite. The properties include grain or crystal size, hardness, texture, colour and chemical reactions.

Rock	Photo	Appearance	Porous or non-porous?	Does it fizz in acid?
limestone		A pale, hard rock. It often contains fossils.	usually porous	yes
sandstone		A yellow rock made of grains of sand.	usually porous	no
marble		A hard rock that is normally white. It is made of crystals and usually has no fossils or layers.	non-porous	yes
basalt		A hard, dark rock with very small crystals. There are no layers.	non-porous	no
granite		A hard rock with large crystals. There are no layers.	non-porous	no

c List the five rocks in the table, and say whether each is igneous, sedimentary or metamorphic.

d How can you tell the difference between limestone and marble?

Questions

1 Copy and complete these sentences.

Rocks in the three groups change from one to another group over _____ of years. Igneous rocks are made from molten rock called _____. Small grains that become pressed together into layers turn into _____ rock. Rocks can become buried, and under heat and over increased pressure they can change into _____ rock.

2 Write the following parts of the rock cycle in the correct order, starting with weathering and erosion.

weathering and erosion   deposition   igneous rocks form   sedimentary rocks form   burying and squeezing   volcanic eruption   metamorphic rocks form   rocks melt

3 Imagine you are a pebble on a beach. Prepare a poster to describe the story of your life.

For your notes:

● The three main groups of rock, igneous, sedimentary and metamorphic, are made in different ways and have different properties.

● They may change from one group to another over millions of years.

● These changes are summarised in the **rock cycle**.

Why and what?

These words are all question words.
Questions are very important in science:

Why?

What?

How?

Which?

Where?

● Scientists carry out investigations to find out the answers to questions. It is important to ask the right kinds of questions if you want to find out anything useful.

● Scientists use questions when they are classifying things and putting them into groups. A **key** is a set of questions that helps us to classify things.

Out in the field

Class 8T are on a geology field trip. They are looking at the rocks around them and testing them with acid. They are collecting small samples of different rocks to take back to the classroom. There they will find out about the properties of each rock, so they can look up in a reference book what sort of rock it is.

Before they go, Lisa, Grant and Hassan discuss the kinds of questions they will need to ask and answer about each rock sample. Read their suggestions.

We need to ask: 'What colour is the rock?' We could ask: 'What are the crystals like?'

How about asking: 'Does it react with acid?' 'What is the rock made up of?' 'Does the rock have crystals?'

We need to know: 'Is it made up of grains?' We can ask: 'Does the rock have any layers in it?'

ⓐ In your group, consider each of the questions they suggest. Decide which questions would be the most useful when identifying rocks.

ⓑ Try to explain why each of the useful questions will be useful.

ⓒ See if you can come up with some more useful questions in your group.

Identifying the rocks

Look at these photos of the rocks Hassan's group brought back.

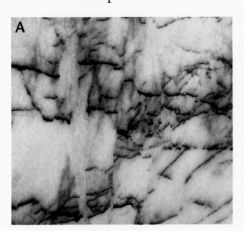 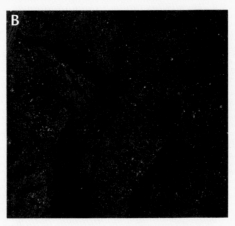 

d Use the useful questions to help you to identify each of the three rocks.

Back at the classroom, Lisa's group found they hadn't kept careful enough notes about their samples. To make matters worse, Lisa had felt ill by the end of the field trip and had gone straight home. She took their group's three rock samples with her.

The rest of the group put together the notes they had. These are shown on the right.

e Look at the information Lisa's group brought back. Draw up a table with headings for the different properties rocks have. Look back at page 81 to remind you. Make three rows numbered 1 to 3 for their three rock samples.

f From the notes Lisa's group brought back, write in your table under the correct property what you already know about the three rock samples.

g Look at the gaps in your table where you don't have any information. In your group, write down the questions you would need to answer in order to find out about the properties of the rock and identify it.

1. Pale orange rock. May contain small bits of shells.

2. Contains pink, white and grey coloured bits in the rock. Doesn't react with acid.

3. Contains small black crystals. Very hard.

Questions

1 Write a key to classify the three main groups of rock – sedimentary, igneous and metamorphic. Use your table and the questions you have written, and what you know about the properties of these three main groups of rock.

2 Discuss what kinds of questions are best for classifying things. Explain your answer.

3 Why is it important to record observations from a field trip carefully?

I1 What temperature?

Temperature

It's hot in here!

It's cold in here!

The hall feels hot to Stephen and cold to Miriam. What is hot to one person may be cold to another. We can't depend on our bodies to tell us how hot things are.

We use **temperature** to decide how hot something is. We measure temperature in **degrees Celsius**, or °C, using a thermometer. On the Celsius scale, freezing water is 0°C and boiling water is 100°C.

How hot?

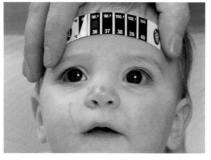

The temperature of the human body is 37°C.

Ice melts and water freezes at 0°C.

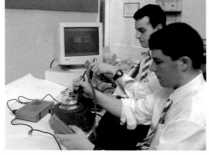

Water boils and condenses at 100°C. Ethanol boils and condenses at 79°C.

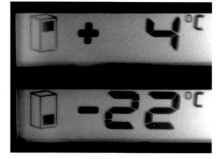

Fridges are kept at 4°C. Freezers are kept at −22°C.

Hot, not cold

Stephen is right. There is no such thing as 'cold'. To understand about 'hot' and 'cold' we need to talk about **energy**. Hot things contain a lot of heat energy or **thermal energy**. Cold things contain less thermal energy (heat energy).

There's no such thing as cold.

Shut the door, don't let the cold in.

Shut the door. Don't let the heat out!

Imagine Stephen touching something hot, like a radiator. The thermal energy moves from the radiator, which is hotter, to his hand, which is colder. Stephen decides the radiator is hot because the thermal energy flows into his hand.

Imagine Stephen touching something cold, like an ice cube. The thermal energy moves from his hand, which is hotter, to the ice cube, which is colder. Stephen decides that the ice cube is cold because thermal energy leaves his hand.

When Stephen's dad said, 'Don't let the heat out!' he should have said, 'Don't let the thermal energy out!'

Questions

1 Copy and complete these sentences by pairing up the correct beginnings and ends.

Beginnings	**Ends**
There are 100 °C between …	… at 0 °C.
Things feel hot because …	… thermal energy flows out of our skin.
Water freezes and melts …	… at 100 °C.
The scientific word for heat is …	… thermal energy.
Things feel cold because …	… thermal energy flows into our skin.
Water boils and condenses …	… freezing water and boiling water.

2 a Write down all the temperatures mentioned on these pages.

  b Put them in a list with the hottest at the top and the coldest at the bottom.

  c Write the name of an object at each temperature. For example, 0 °C freezing water.

For your notes:

- We measure **temperature** in **degrees Celsius, °C**.

- Freezing water is 0 °C. Boiling water is 100 °C.

- The scientific name for heat is **thermal energy**.

How long?

Stephen makes a cup of coffee. He only fills the kettle to the 'two cup' mark. The kettle takes just over one minute to boil.

Later, everyone wants a hot drink. Stephen fills the kettle to the 'full' mark. The kettle takes almost five minutes to boil. Stephen's little sister, Ellen, wonders why it took longer to boil when the temperature rise is the same.

a **The tap water was at 20°C. What is the temperature rise both times?**

Explaining heating

These 20 children represent the particles of water in the part filled kettle. Each child has 2p to represent the starting temperature, which is 20°C.

These 100 children represent the particles of water in the full kettle. Each child has 2p to represent the starting temperature, which is 20°C.

The two cartoons represent different amounts of water. Giving each child an extra 8p represents heating the water from 20°C to 100°C. For the smaller amount of water you have to put in 160p (160 = 20 × 8). For the larger amount of water you have to put in 800p (800 = 100 × 8). If there is more water you have to put in more energy to get the same temperature rise. This is why it took more time.

b **Which needed more energy, heating the part-full kettle to 100°C, or heating the full kettle to 100°C?**

Taking it further

The 'money and children' model is a useful way of thinking about energy and particles. We can use it to see the difference between energy and temperature.

> ### Do you remember?
>
> Water, like all materials, is made up of particles. Read about particles on page ix to remind you.

Temperature and energy are not the same thing. The temperature is the energy per particle, shown in the cartoons as the money per child. When we think about energy we have to think about the particles and the temperature. Hotter does not always mean more energy. There can be more energy but a lower temperature.

C Think again about the part-full and full kettles.

5p each represents a temperature of 50 °C. Total money or 'energy' is 10p.

2p each represents a temperature of 20 °C. Total money or 'energy' is 12p.

  (i) Which would be hotter after one minute of heating?

  (ii) Which would contain more energy when it was boiling?

Strange thought

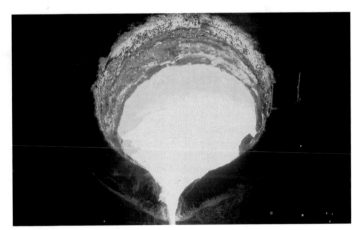

There is more energy in an iceberg …

… than in this white-hot molten iron.

Questions

1 Copy and complete these sentences.

  a Temperature is measured in …
  b The energy per particle is the …
  c It takes more energy to increase the temperature if there are more …

2 Which of these will contain more energy?
Give a reason for your answer.

  a 10 cm³ water at 20 °C or 100 cm³ water at 20 °C?
  b 10 cm³ water at 90 °C or 10 cm³ water at 30 °C?
  c 1 g iron at 40 °C or 10 000 g iron at 20 °C?

For your notes:

● Temperature is the energy per particle.

● Smaller, hotter things can have less energy than colder, larger things.

Allow for it

Railway tracks are made with gaps. The gaps allow them to get bigger on a hot day without bending out of shape.

We say that materials **expand** when they are heated.

The cables in this photo on the right are made of aluminium. The cables are not tight between the pylons. This allows them to get shorter in the winter.

We say that materials **contract** when they are cooled.

ⓐ Why do we need gaps in railway tracks?

Expanding

Why do solids expand? We need to think about the particles.

When you heat a solid you give it thermal energy. You give the particles more energy. The particles vibrate more.

Look at the diagram on the right. When the particles vibrate more they take up more space. The solid expands.

ⓑ Explain why heating a solid makes it expand.

Liquids too

Jenny and Dan have made their own thermometer, like the one in the photo at the top of page 89. They have filled a flask with coloured water and put a glass tube in the top.

Do you remember?

Brush up your knowledge of particles by reading page ix.

When they heat the flask the liquid rises up the tube. The liquid expands. When they cool the flask, the liquid level falls. It contracts.

Again, we can explain this using the particle model. When the liquid is heated the particles are given more energy. The particles vibrate more. This means that each particle takes up more space. The liquid expands.

c Explain why a liquid contracts when it is cooled.

Gases

Jed has bought helium-filled balloons for his party. The balloons are delivered in the morning, when it is cool. By noon most of the balloons have burst. Jed is not impressed. He wants a refund.

The helium gas has heated up and expanded. The person filling the balloons has not left enough space for this expansion, so the balloons burst.

When a gas is heated the particles move more quickly. This makes the gas expand because the gaps between the particles increase.

d A balloon full of air is put in the fridge.
 (i) Will the balloon contract or expand?
 (ii) Will the particles become further apart or closer together?

Questions

1 Copy and complete these sentences using the words below.

 gases   solids   expand   liquids   space   further

 Solids, gases and liquids all _____ when they are heated. _____ and _____ expand because the particles vibrate more and take up more _____. _____ expand because the particles get _____ apart.

2 Write your own sentences explaining why solids, liquids and gases contract when they are cooled. Use your answer to **1** to help you.

3 Why does a metal ruler give a different measurement on a cold day than on a hot day?

For your notes:

- Materials **expand** when heated and **contract** when cooled.

- A solid or a liquid expands when heated because the particles vibrate more and take up more space. The opposite happens during contraction.

- Gases expand when heated: the gaps between the particles get bigger. The opposite happens during contraction.

14 All change

Watching ice melt

Darren and Jackie are heating ice from the freezer. The apparatus they use is shown in the diagram on the right.

a What are they using to:
(i) heat the ice?
(ii) measure the temperature?

The computer draws the graph below.

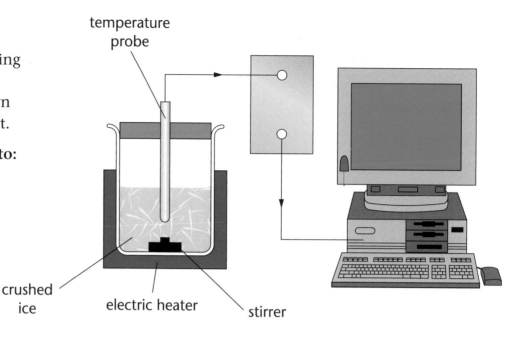

temperature probe

crushed ice

electric heater

stirrer

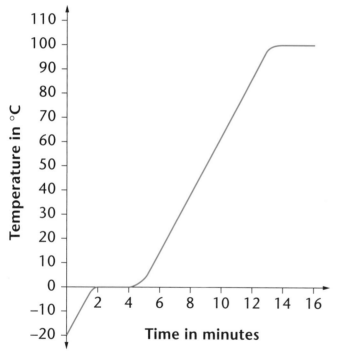

That's weird. It's got flat bits. Perhaps the equipment stopped working.

Look, the flat bits are at 0 °C and 100 °C. It goes flat during melting and boiling.

Particles

Darren and Jackie then think about what the water particles are doing during their experiment. They use the information on pages 88–89 to help them. They make the poster on page 91.

Reverse it

When you put energy in you get melting and boiling. When you take energy out you get condensing and freezing.

Do you remember?

The melting point is the temperature where you get melting and freezing. The boiling point is the temperature where you get boiling and condensing.

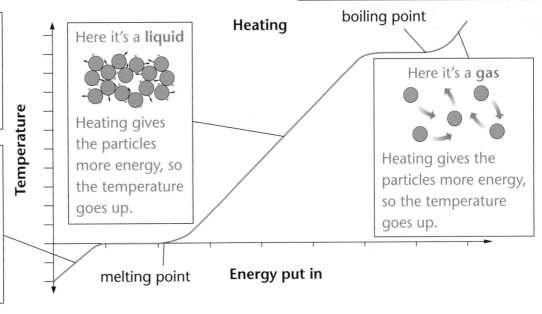

The three **states of matter** are solid, liquid and gas. Melting and boiling are **changes in state**, so are freezing and condensing.

Here it's a **solid**

Heating gives the particles more energy so the temperature goes up.

Here it's a **liquid**

Heating gives the particles more energy, so the temperature goes up.

Here it's a **gas**

Heating gives the particles more energy, so the temperature goes up.

Temperature

Heating

boiling point

melting point

Energy put in

1 You put energy in all the time …

2 … but sometimes it doesn't show up in the temperature.

3 The energy isn't giving the particles more energy.

4 The energy goes into breaking the particles apart instead.

5 This happens during melting and boiling. That's why you get the flat bits in the graph.

b Name the three states of matter.

c What happens to the temperature when you give the particles more energy?

d During melting and boiling, the extra energy is not raising the temperature. What is the energy doing?

Questions

1 Copy and complete these sentences by pairing up the correct beginnings and ends.

Beginnings

To melt or boil something …
When you give the particles more energy …
When the energy is breaking the particles apart during melting or boiling …

Ends

… the temperature goes up.
… you have to put energy in.

… the temperature doesn't go up.

2 Copy and complete these sentences about cooling, condensation and freezing.

   a To condense or freeze something …

   b When you take energy away from the particles the temperature …

   c You don't get a drop in temperature during …

For your notes:

- The **changes of state** are melting, boiling, condensing and freezing.

- Melting and boiling happen when you put energy in. Condensation and freezing happen when you take energy out.

- During changes in state the temperature of a substance stays the same.

15 Conduction

Learn about:
- Moving heat energy in solids
- Conductors and insulators

Heat it up

Stephen's dad forgot to take the chicken out the freezer. Dinner is going to be very late unless they can get the chicken defrosted quickly. It has to be totally defrosted before they can cook it.

ⓐ What could Stephen's dad do to defrost the chicken?

Conduction in solids

Thermal energy moves through solids, like the chicken, by **conduction**. In conduction, thermal energy moves from particle to particle.

We can use our 'children and money' model to explain conduction. Remember, the children are the particles and the energy is the money.

ⓑ (i) What do the children represent?
(ii) What does the money represent?
(iii) The diagrams on the right show conduction in a solid. Why can't the children holding money change places?

ⓒ Think again about the chicken. When will the chicken stop warming up?

Conductors and insulators

We have to get heat from the surroundings into the chicken.

Do you remember?

The scientific word for heat is thermal energy.

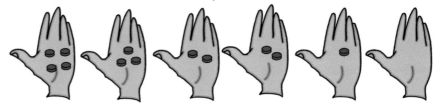

One end of the solid is heated up.

The energy is passed from particle to particle by conduction.

After conduction each particle has the same energy – all parts of the solid are at the same temperature.

Unwrap it and take it off the polystyrene tray. Plastic is an insulator.

Put it on the metal draining board and cover it in foil. The metal is a good conductor.

Some materials conduct thermal energy better than others. The stainless steel draining board and the aluminium foil are good **thermal conductors**. Other materials conduct thermal energy poorly – we call these **thermal insulators**. The cling film and the polystyrene tray are thermal insulators.

Conduction in non-solids

The particles have to be touching for conduction to work. Look at the diagrams on the right showing the particles in a solid, a liquid and a gas. In the liquid, each particle touches fewer other particles than in a solid. Conduction works better in solids than liquids.

In the gas the particles are far apart. Very little conduction happens in gases.

There are some places where there are no particles at all. We call a place with no particles a **vacuum**. Conduction does not happen in a vacuum, because there aren't any particles.

Mix it up

Non-metallic materials that contain gas pockets are very good thermal insulators. Expanded polystyrene, like the tray holding the chicken, is this type of material. So are fluffed-up feathers and woolly jumpers.

d What type of material are the foil and the draining board?

e What type of material are the tray and the cling film?

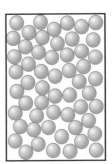
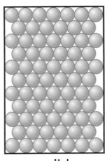

solid   liquid

gas   vacuum

Both the feathers and the air trapped between them are good insulators.

Questions

1 Copy and complete these sentences using the words below.

   cooler   hotter   particle   energy   touching

   Conduction is when _____ is passed from _____ to particle. The particles need to be _____. The energy moves from the _____ parts of the material to the _____ parts of the material.

2 Copy and arrange the words below in order, with the best thermal conductor at the top of your list and the best thermal insulator at the bottom.

   vacuum   water   air   aluminium   plastic

3 Explain why kebabs cook more quickly on metal skewers than:

   a with no skewers   **b** on wooden skewers.

For your notes:

- Thermal energy is transferred from hotter objects to cooler objects.

- During **conduction** energy is transferred from one particle to the particles touching it.

- Some materials are better **thermal conductors** than others. Poor conductors are called **thermal insulators**.

- Solids are better conductors than liquids and gases.

93

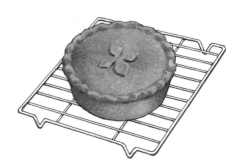

Moving air

Think about a hot pie taken out of the oven and left to cool on a wire rack. The pie is surrounded by air. Air is a poor conductor, but the pie still cools. The thermal energy is carried away from the pie by **convection**.

Convection happens in gases and liquids, but not in solids. This is because gases and liquids change shape and flow.

a **Why doesn't convection happen in solids?**

Convection currents

When the hot air rises cooler air takes its place. Think about the pie. The air above the pie is heated. The warmer air then rises, as shown by the red arrows in the diagram on the right. Cooler air moves in to take the place of the warmer air. This shown by the blue arrows.

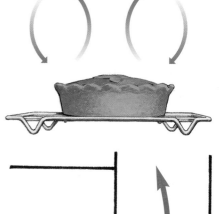

This circular movement of air is called a **convection current**.

b **How many convection currents are shown in the diagram?**

Look at the drawing on the right of the fireplace with the chimney. The hot air above the fire rises, and cooler air is drawn into the room to take its place. There is a convection current.

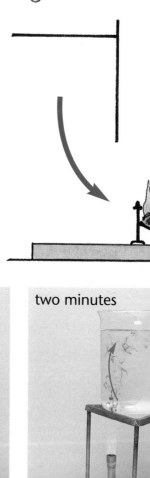

This is very important if you have an open fire. The fire needs fresh air all the time, or it will use up all the oxygen in the room.

If you have central heating rather than an open fire, you should block up the chimney. Warm air will rise up the chimney, taking with it all the heat energy you have paid for.

Convection in liquids

Convection also happens in liquids. Look at the photos on the right. They show a beaker of water being heated. The flame of the Bunsen burner is pointing at the left of the beaker, so only the water there is being heated.

Purple dye has been added so that you can see the movement of the water.

one minute   two minutes

c How can you see the hot water rising in the beaker?

By two minutes the dye is moving across the top of the beaker. This shows the convection current in the liquid. Thermal energy is being transferred through the water by convection.

d What would happen to the purple dye by the time the water boils?

Thinking about convection

We can use our 'children with money' model to think about convection. Remember, the children are the particles and the money is energy.

In convection the particles move. You can imagine children picking up money at one table and walking across the room to put the money down on another table. The transfer stops once there is the same amount of money (or energy) in both places.

e In the cartoon, which table represents the higher temperature?

f Think carefully about the particles in a solid. Why can't a solid transfer energy by convection?

Questions

1 Copy and complete these sentences using the words below.

rises   falls   temperature   thermal   gases   liquids   solids

_____ energy can be transferred by convection. Convection happens in _____ and _____ but not in _____.

Convection currents happen when there is a _____ difference. Hotter liquid or gas _____ and cooler liquid or gas _____.

2 Describe how a heater on one side of a room can heat the air in the whole room. Use the words below.

air   rise   fall   hotter   cooler   convection current   mix

3 Use the 'children and money' model of energy transfer to explain the differences between convection and conduction.

For your notes:

- In **convection** the particles move, transferring the thermal energy.

- Convection happens in gases and liquids, but not in solids.

- A **convection current** happens when one part of a gas or liquid is hotter than another part.

Evaporation, radiation

Learn about:
● Cooling by evaporation
● Moving energy by radiation

Suddenly cooler

You cool down very quickly if you stand around while you are wet. This cooling is because water is **evaporating** from our skin.

It takes energy to evaporate a liquid into a gas. The particles in a gas move faster than the particles in a liquid. This extra energy has to come from somewhere.

Also, the particles in a liquid are held together. It takes energy to break apart the particles in a liquid, so they are free to move as part of a gas.

The energy to turn the liquid into a gas is taken from our skin. That is why we cool down when we sweat.

ⓐ **What two things happen to the particles in a liquid when they become part of a gas?**

This wine cooler also cools by evaporation. Water evaporates from tiny holes in the pottery surface. The energy needed to evaporate the water comes from the wine inside, so the wine cools down.

ⓑ **Where does the energy come from to:**
   (i) evaporate sweat from our skin?
   (ii) evaporate water from a cup of tea?

Radiation

Thermal energy is transferred from the Sun to the Earth. How does this happen?

There is only empty space, a vacuum, between the Earth and the Sun. That means the energy cannot be passed from particle to particle, as in conduction. It cannot be carried by moving particles, as in convection.

There has to be another way of transferring thermal energy.

The thermal energy is transferred by **radiation**. **Infrared radiation** carries thermal energy from the Sun to the Earth.

Any hot object gives out infrared radiation. Look at the photo on the left of people running away from the police at night. The picture was taken with an infrared camera, which picks up infrared radiation rather than light. The people show up brightly, because they are sources of infrared radiation.

c The Earth is not heated by conduction or convection.
  (i) Why not?
  (ii) What type of thermal energy transfer heats the Earth?

Thinking about radiation

We can think about radiation using the 'children with money' model. Look at the cartoon on the right. No children cross the gap, only the energy crosses the gap.

d In the model what represents:
  (i)   the hot object?
  (ii) the cooler object?
  (iii) the energy?

Questions

1 Copy and complete these sentences using the words below.

> **vacuum   hotter   cooler   infrared   liquid   gas
> radiation   energy   thermal   evaporation**

Energy is transferred away from liquids by _____.
The particles with the most _____ leave the _____ and become part of a _____.

_____ _____ is like light. It can travel through many materials and across a _____. It transfers _____ energy from a _____ object to a _____ object.

2 Look at this diagram of the cup of tea cooling. Write out each word below and pair it up with the correct colour arrows.

⟶   **radiation**

⟶   **convection**

⟶   **evaporation**

⟶   **conduction**

For your notes:

- Thermal energy can be transferred from a liquid by **evaporation**. The liquid then cools its surroundings.

- **Radiation** happens when thermal energy is transferred by **infrared radiation**, which is like light.

Think about:
● Changing more than one variable
● Explaining your results

18 Explaining the results

Raising the temperature

Ellen and Sean heated different sized blocks of three different metals. They wanted to find out how much energy it takes to raise the temperature of the metals by 40°C, from 25°C to 65°C.

Sean plotted a scatter graph of their results. His graph is shown below. Ellen and Sean discussed what lines to put on their graph.

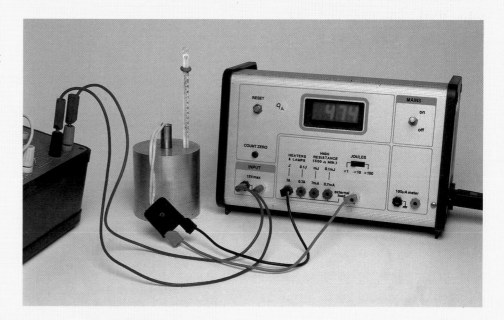

Sean did not think there was a pattern, and he did not want to draw lines on the graph. Ellen thought there should be three lines – one for copper, one for aluminium and one for tin.

ⓐ Who do you agree with, Sean or Ellen? Give reasons for your answer.

ⓑ How does increasing the mass used change the energy neededed to heat the block?

ⓒ How does changing the metal used change the energy needed to heat the block?

ⓓ Use the graph (without drawing on the book) to estimate how much energy would be needed to heat 200 g of aluminium by 40°C.

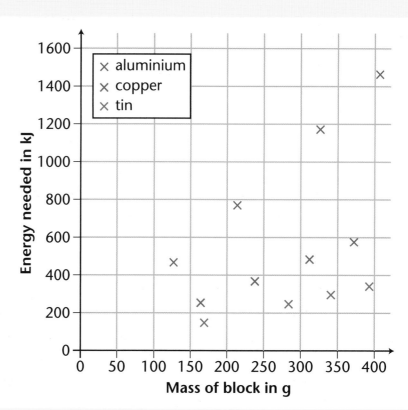

Explaining the results

Mr Smith, their teacher, asks the pupils to suggest why 300 kJ will heat only 83 g of aluminium by 40 °C, but 346 g of tin and 194 g of copper.

> *I think that the metals are just different. Perhaps the particles are different.*

> *I think aluminium loses a lot of energy while you are trying to heat it up. The tin keeps the energy in better, so you can warm up lots of it.*

e **Who do you agree with, Sean or Ellen? Give reasons for your answer.**

They decide that Ellen's idea is easier to test than Sean's. They repeat the experiment shown in the photo on page 98, only this time they wrap up the metal blocks in layers of insulation to keep the thermal energy in.

They still get different results for tin, copper and aluminium. It still takes more energy to heat the aluminium and less energy to heat the tin.

f **Does this experiment suggest that Ellen's idea was correct? Explain your answer.**

g **Does this experiment provide any evidence to support Sean's idea? Give reasons for your answer.**

Questions

1 Think about what happens to the particles in a solid when you heat them.

  a Which vibrate more, the particles in a cooler solid, or the particles in a warmer solid?

  b Tin particles have a much bigger mass than aluminium particles. They weigh more than four times as much. Sean suggests that metals with lighter atoms need more energy to heat them up. Do you agree with Sean's idea? Why?

2 Copper particles weigh more than twice as much as aluminium particles, but only about half as much as tin particles. Look back at the graph on page 98.

  a Which takes more energy to heat up, tin or copper?

  b Which takes more energy to heat up, copper or aluminium?

  c Do you think this evidence supports Sean's idea? Give your reason.

J1 Magnetic fields

There is a pulling force between magnets and some metals. The magnet **attracts** the metal. The attraction between the fridge magnets and the fridge door holds them on.

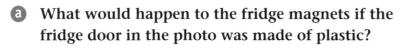

Do you remember?

Iron and steel are attracted to magnets. Most metals and all non-metals are not attracted to magnets.

a What would happen to the fridge magnets if the fridge door in the photo was made of plastic?

b Aluminium drinks cans can be recycled, but not steel ones. How can you decide if your drink can is steel or aluminium?

Magnetic magic

Iron and steel are called **magnetic materials**. They are attracted to a magnet. The only other metals that are magnetic are nickel and cobalt. Iron oxide is also a magnetic material.

Magnets attract magnetic materials. They can also attract each other. But sometimes the same magnets push away from each other. They **repel** each other.

Look at this photo of a spinning top. It is floating in the air. It looks as if there is nothing holding it up! The magnets in the base are repelling the magnets in the spinning top. The magnetic force balances the weight of the top, so it floats.

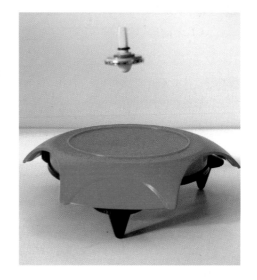

Why do magnets sometimes attract and sometimes repel? The reason is that magnets have two different ends, or **poles**. One end is called the **north pole** and the other end is called the **south pole**.

- If you bring the north pole of one magnet towards the south pole of another magnet they attract each other.

- If you bring the north poles of two magnets together they repel each other. Two south poles together also repel.

Opposite poles attract, like poles repel.

Magnetic fields

Magnets do not only attract or repel at their poles. They pull or push in the space all around them. This space is called a **magnetic field**.

The magnetic field is invisible but we can see where it is by using tiny bits of iron called **iron filings**. Look at the photo on the right. We sprinkle iron filings on a piece of paper on top of a **bar magnet**. The iron filings make lines. The lines show the magnetic field around the magnet.

These lines are called **magnetic field lines**. They are shown in the diagram below right. They are closer together nearer the magnet. This shows that the magnetic field is stronger here.

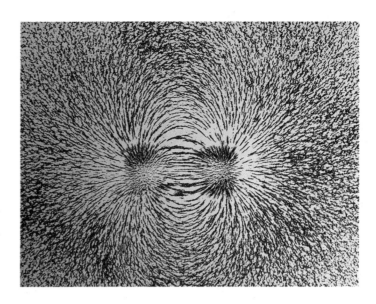

c What happens to the iron filings when you put them into a magnetic field?

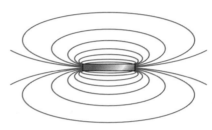

Questions

1 Copy and complete these sentences by pairing up the correct beginnings and endings.

Beginnings	Endings
Magnets have two ends called …	… are all magnetic materials.
The closer you are to the magnet …	… and like poles repel.
Where magnets push or pull is called …	… the north pole and south pole.
Iron, steel, cobalt, nickel and iron oxide …	… the stronger the magnetic field.
Unlike poles attract …	… a magnetic field.

2 You have a 2p coin (made using a lot of nickel), a silver spoon, an aluminium saucepan, a plastic fork and a steel key. Which of them will be attracted to a magnet?

3 Answer the following questions about magnetic field lines.

   a Where do you get them?
   b How do you show them?
   c What do they tell you about the strength of the magnetic field?

For your notes:

- Iron, steel, cobalt, nickel and iron oxide are all **magnetic materials**.

- Magnets have a **north pole** and a **south pole**.

- Like poles **repel**, opposite poles **attract**.

- The space around a magnet where it pushes and pulls is called a **magnetic field**.

- The magnetic field is stronger closer to the magnet.

Learn about:
- The Earth's magnetism
- The direction of magnetic fields

The Earth's magnetic field

William Gilbert lived when Elizabeth I was Queen of England. He was the first scientist who investigated magnetism. He worked out that if a magnet was floating freely it always pointed north.

He decided that the Earth was a giant bar magnet, with a huge magnetic field. He published his conclusion in 1600. The diagram shows the magnetic field of the Earth.

You can use a **compass** to stop you getting lost. A compass needle is a magnet that can move around freely. The north pole of the needle is pointed, so you know where north is.

ⓐ **Which way does the south pole of the compass needle point?**

North Pole

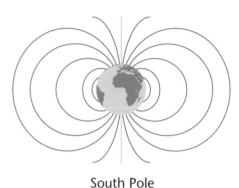

South Pole

A ship's compass from the 1600s.

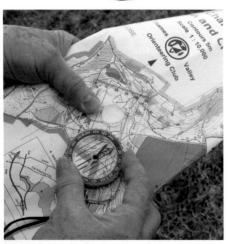

You may have noticed two facts that don't seem to fit together:

- The north pole of a magnet points north (towards the North Pole).

- Opposite poles attract. A north pole of a magnet is attracted to the south pole of another magnet.

The idea that came first was that north means at the top of a map, or towards the North Pole. Then magnets were discovered. The end of the magnet that pointed north was called the north pole of the magnet.

So the 'big magnet' inside the Earth has its south pole in the north, and its north pole in the south. Very confusing! Sometimes science is like that. Blame the person who called the end of a magnet that pointed north a 'north pole'!

Navigating

Having a compass made it much easier for sailors to find their way, or **navigate**. Before compasses, the sailors found their way using the Sun and stars. Bad weather meant they could not see the Sun or the stars, and they often got lost. A compass like the one in this photo works whatever the weather.

ⓑ **Why does a compass work in all types of weather?**

Which way does the field go?

A compass always points to the Earth's North Pole unless you hold it very close to another magnet. Then the pointed end of the compass is attracted to the south pole of the magnet.

We can use a compass to show us the directions of the magnetic field lines around a bar magnet.

The photo below shows compasses close to a bar magnet.

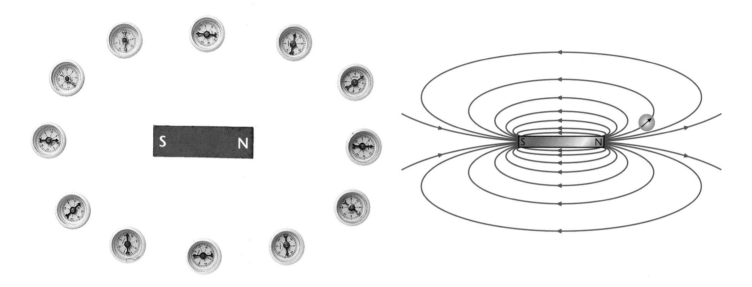

c Look closely at this photo. Draw a diagram showing clearly where each compass needle is pointing.

The compasses point along the magnetic field lines. The magnetic field lines start at the north pole of the bar magnet and end up at the south pole of the bar magnet. The arrows show the direction of the field lines in the diagram above right.

For your notes:

- The Earth is like a huge magnet. It has a magnetic field.

- A **compass** always points north unless there is a magnet close by.

- A compass close to a magnet points along the magnetic field lines.

- Magnetic field lines run from the north pole of a magnet to its south pole.

Questions

1 Copy and complete these sentences.

The Earth acts as a huge _____. It has a _____ field. People can navigate on Earth using a _____. It has a needle which points north.

2 a Why is a compass better than the Sun and stars for navigating?
   b If you are navigating with a compass, why do you need to keep other magnets away from it?

Natural magnets

We know people used magnets as long ago as 500 BC. They used a natural magnet called **lodestone**.

Lodestone is iron oxide and it is found in rocks. It acts as a magnet. Hundreds of years ago people used pieces of lodestone hung from a thread as the first compasses.

Lodestone.

Making magnets

There is not enough lodestone in the world to give us all the magnets we need. We need to make more.

Magnetic materials can act like magnets. Look at the photo of the magnet picking up paperclips. A paperclip that is touching the magnet picks up more paperclips. It acts as part of the magnet.

If the paperclip was made of iron, it would go back to normal as soon as it was separated from the magnet. Iron can only be a **temporary magnet**.

Other magnetic materials can be made into **permanent magnets**. They stay as magnets for many, many years. Iron oxide makes excellent permanent magnets.

You can make a magnet using a steel needle. Steel can make a weak permanent magnet. You can use it as a compass needle.

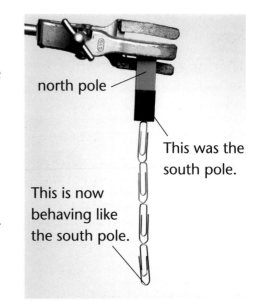

north pole

This was the south pole.

This is now behaving like the south pole.

a Name a magnetic material that:
(i) makes a strong permanent magnet
(ii) makes a weak permanent magnet
(iii) only makes a temporary magnet.

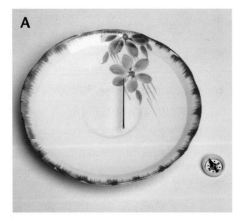

A

Making a compass

To make a compass needle you stroke a steel needle with one pole of a strong magnet. You have to stroke it several times and always in the same direction. The magnetic field of the strong magnet makes the needle into a magnet.

The photos **A** to **C** show this process. In photo **A** a steel needle is floating in a saucer of water. You can see from the compass next to it that it is not pointing in any particular direction.

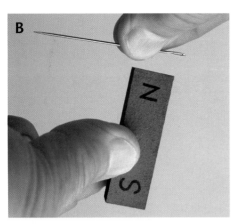

In photo **B** the needle is made into a magnet by stroking it with one pole of a magnet.

In photo **C** the magnetised needle is floating in water. You can see by the compass next to it that it is now pointing north.

b Why do we need to float the needle on water?

c What happened to the needle when it was stroked with a magnet?

Magnetic or magnet?

There is a test to tell the difference between a magnet and a piece of magnetic material. Magnets can repel. Magnetic materials are always attracted to a magnet.

John had five lumps of different materials. He was told that two of them were magnets. He got a strong, permanent magnet. He tested each lump with the north pole of the magnet and the south pole of the magnet. The table shows John's results.

Lump	1	2	3	4	5
Test with N pole of magnet	attracted	repelled	attracted	attracted	attracted
Test with S pole of magnet	attracted	attracted	attracted	attracted	repelled

d Which two lumps were magnets? Explain your answer.

Questions

1 Copy and complete these sentences by pairing up the correct beginnings and endings.

Beginnings	Endings
Two magnets can …	… becomes a temporary magnet.
Steel in a magnetic field …	… always attract.
A magnet and some magnetic material …	… becomes a weak permanent magnet.
Iron in a magnetic field …	… attract and repel.

2 Describe how you would make a steel needle into a compass.

For your notes:

- We can make magnets from magnetic materials by putting them in a magnetic field.

- Iron can only form a **temporary magnet**. Iron oxide makes a **permanent magnet**.

- Only magnets repel other magnets.

J4 Electromagnets

Electromagnets

The photo on the right shows an **electromagnet**. It is being used to pick up magnetic materials in a scrapyard.

Electromagnets are magnets made using electricity. They can be switched on and off. This makes them very useful.

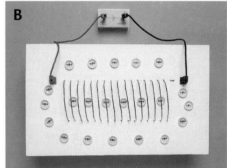

(a) Name three metals the electromagnet will not pick up.

(b) Look at the photo. What will happen when the electromagnet is switched off?

Making electromagnets

You get a magnetic field if you put an electric current through a coil of wire. Photo **A** shows the magnetic field around a coil using iron filings. You can see that its shape is very similar to the one around a bar magnet.

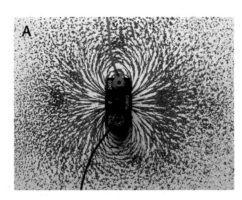

A

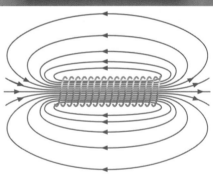

B

The direction of the magnetic field is also the same as for a bar magnet. You can see this in photo **B** using compasses.

The magnetic field only happens when there is a current in the wire. When you switch the current off, the magnetic field goes away.

(c) Look at photo B. Which way will all the compasses point when the current is switched off?

Making it stronger

The magnetic field around the coil is very weak. You can make it stronger by putting a piece of iron, called a **core**, inside the coil. This makes an electromagnet. There is an electromagnet in the photo on the right. It is strong enough to lift the keys.

(d) What would happen to the keys if you switched the current off?

Iron is better than steel for the core. Steel stays magnetised after the current is switched off, so the electromagnet does not switch off properly.

Gina and Scott wanted to make their electromagnet stronger. A strong electromagnet picks up more paperclips. They increased the number of turns in the coil but they kept the current the same (they used 0.5 A). The table above shows their results.

Number of turns	10	20	30	40	50
Paperclips lifted	3	9	16	31	40

e Copy and complete this sentence. 'As the number of turns in the coil increases, the strength of the electromagnet ...'

Ruksham and Hannah also wanted to make their electromagnet stronger. They increased the current by adding more cells to their circuit. This table shows their results.

Current in A	0.2	0.4	0.6	0.8	1.0
Paperclips lifted	5	11	16	24	29

Their results show that increasing the current increases the strength of the electromagnet.

f Suggest two variables Rucksham and Hannah would have kept the same in their investigation.

So there are three ways of making an electromagnet stronger:

- use an iron core
- increase the numbers of turns in the coil
- increase the current.

Using electromagnets

Electromagnets can repel as well as attract. Look at this photo. There is an electromagnet in the train and another in the track. They repel, so the train 'floats'. This means there is no friction between the train and the rail, so it only takes a small amount of force to push the train along.

Questions

1 Copy and complete these sentences using the words below.

number of turns   magnetic field   current   iron core

A coil of wire has a _____ _____ around it when the current is switched on.

An electromagnet has an _____ _____ inside. You can make an electromagnet stronger by increasing the _____ _____ _____ in the coil, or increasing the _____.

2 Why is an electromagnet often more useful than an ordinary magnet?

For your notes:

- A coil of wire with a current in it forms a magnetic field. It is the same shape as the magnetic field around a bar magnet.

- If you put an iron **core** in the coil, you make an **electromagnet**.

- A electromagnet can be made stronger by using more turns of wire in the coil and/or a larger current.

Think about:
- Controlling variables
- Analysing results

A multitude of variables

Priya's class is doing an investigation into electromagnets. Their teacher, Mrs Futter, asks them about the possible variables. She writes their suggestions on the board.

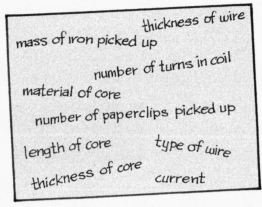

mass of iron picked up
thickness of wire
number of turns in coil
material of core
number of paperclips picked up
length of core
type of wire
thickness of core
current

Do you remember?

An input (or independent) variable is something you change. An outcome (or dependent) variable is something you measure.

(a) **Write the variables in two lists: input (or independent) variables and outcome (or dependent) variables. (*Hint:* there are only two outcome variables in the list.)**

Key variables

Mrs Futter then asks them to pick out the **key variables** from the input (or independent) variables. She explains that a key variable has a large effect on the strength of the electromagnet.

(b) **Use your knowledge of electromagnets to pick out three key input variables.**

Heidi and Priya pick different key input variables.

(c) **What should Heidi and Priya do about the other input variables? Explain your answer.**

Number of turns in coil. The more turns, the more magnetic field.

Material of core. I know that iron makes a good core, but I want to know if other metals work as well.

Heidi

Priya

Priya has no problems planning her investigation. But Heidi discovers that the cores are all different sizes and shapes. She decides to continue with her investigation, using different shaped cores.

Outcome variables

Mrs Futter shows the class two different ways of measuring the strength of the electromagnet.

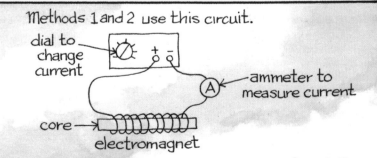

Methods 1 and 2 use this circuit.

dial to change current

ammeter to measure current

core → electromagnet

(1) Use the electromagnet to pick up paperclips. Count the paperclips.
(2) Weigh a container of tiny washers. Use the electromagnet to pick up some of the washers. Weigh the container again. Work out the mass of washers picked up.

I'll use method 2. The tiny washers weigh less than the paperclips, so method 2 should be better than method 1.

Priya

I may as well use method 1. My results will be just 'yes' or 'no'. The cores are too different to compare the strength of the electromagnets.

Heidi

d Do you agree with Heidi? Explain your answer.

Results

Heidi's results

Core material	iron	aluminium	nickel	steel	copper	zinc
Paperclips lifted	11	0	4	16	0	0

Priya's results

Number of turns	10	20	30	40	50
Mass of iron at start in g	50.0	50.0	50.0	50.0	50.0
Mass of iron at end in g	47.2	40.6	33.8	20.1	10.4
Iron picked up in g	2.8	9.4	16.2	29.9	39.9

Analysing the results

e What type of chart or graph could you use to analyse:
  (i) Heidi's results?
  (ii) Priya's results?
  Explain your answer.

Heidi refuses to draw a graph. She says that the numbers are meaningless, because the cores were all different shapes and masses. She says that all she can tell from her experiment is that you need a magnetic material to make the core of an electromagnet.

f Do you agree with Heidi's conclusion?
  Give reasons for your answer.

g What changes would you make to Heidi's method?

Questions

1 Draw a line graph of Priya's results. Add a line of best fit. Write a conclusion for Priya's experiment.

2 Which is the best method of measuring the outcome variable? Give reasons for your answer.

K1 Seeing the light

Learn about:
- Light travelling
- Detecting light

Away from the source

Light is energy on the move. The light travels away from a light source. Look at the photo of the firework. The firework explodes, giving out energy. People can see the firework display from all sides because the light travels away from the exploding firework in all directions.

Do you remember?

Light comes from a **source**. Light bulbs, flames, TV screens, the Sun and the stars are all light sources. When you block light you get a **shadow**.

a Name five different light sources.

Straight through

Cameras show us that light travels in straight lines. The simplest type of camera is a box with a pinhole at one end and a screen at the other. This is called a **pinhole camera**. The girl in the photo is using a pinhole camera to 'take a picture' of the candle flame.

1 Some of the light from the top of the flame goes through the pinhole.

pinhole in card

2 Some of the light from the bottom of the flame also goes through the pinhole.

screen

3 A picture is made on the screen. This is called an **image**.

4 The image is upside down because light travels in straight lines (as shown by the arrows).

b Imagine using a shorter camera. Would the image be smaller or larger?

c Imagine having two holes rather than one. What would you see on the screen? (*Hint:* one hole makes one image.)

Did you know?

You can build a pinhole camera the size of a room, then stand inside to see the image on one wall. The earliest description of a pinhole camera was by the Chinese philosopher Mo-Ti, 2500 years ago.

Detecting light

You see things because you detect light when it enters your eyes. When the light reaches the back of your eyes, a signal is sent to your brain. **Light sensors** and camera film can also be used to detect light.

How fast?

Light travels from a source to your eyes. It must make this journey very quickly, because it doesn't seem to take any time at all! In fact light, travels at 300 000 kilometres every second. This is true of all light. It does not matter whether the light comes from candles, TVs or the Sun – they all give out light that goes this fast.

The light has to travel a great distance before we can measure the time it takes. Light takes 8.5 minutes to travel from the Sun to the Earth – a distance of 150 million kilometres.

d (i) **How far does light travel in one second?**
(ii) **How long will it take light to travel 600 000 km?**

Light from the next nearest star takes over four years to reach Earth.

Questions

1 Copy and complete the sentences using the words below.

image   fast   source   straight   all   eyes

Light is given out by a _____ and travels in _____ directions. Light travels very, very, very _____.

We see light when it enters our _____.

Light travels in _____ lines. This is why you get a clear but upside-down _____ when you use a pinhole camera.

2 Put statements A–D into the correct order to describe how a pinhole camera works.

A An upside-down image is made on the screen.
B The flame gives out light in all directions.
C Some of the light goes through the screen into the girl's eyes, so she sees the image.
D Some of the light from the flame travels in straight lines through the pinhole.

Did you know?

Light goes 30 million times faster than a man can run, 900 thousand times faster than sound travels and 500 thousand times faster than Concorde flies.

For your notes:

- Light travels away from its **source** in all directions.
- Light travels in straight lines.
- We see because light enters our eyes.
- Light travels very, very quickly.

K2 Which ray?

Light bounces

You look into a mirror to check what you look like. Mirrors work because the light bounces back and enters your eyes. We call this **reflection**. Look at the photo. The light **reflects** off two mirrors, bouncing between them.

Almost all surfaces reflect light, not just mirrors. When you walk into a dark room you see nothing. When you switch on a lamp, you see everything. Light from the lamp reflects off the surfaces and enters your eyes. This lets us see things that do not make light.

a **The Moon is not a source of light. The Sun is a source of light. Explain how we can see the Moon.**

Reflected light

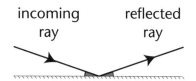

incoming   reflected
ray   ray

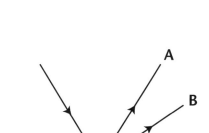

You can use a thin beam of light (a **ray**) to investigate reflection. Look at the diagrams above. A ray of light is hitting a flat surface in each diagram. There is a pattern in the way the ray is reflected.

Look at the angles shown in red. The angle between the ray and the surface is the same for the incoming ray and the reflected ray.

b **Look at the diagram on the right. Which is the correct reflected ray, A, B or C?**

A
B
C

Scattering

The paper of this book looks smooth, but it has many tiny bumps. The photo on the right shows paper seen through a microscope. You can see the tiny bumps.

Look at the diagram. When light hits the paper, it is scattered in all directions. Most surfaces have tiny bumps, like the paper. Most surfaces scatter light.

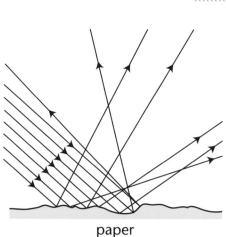

paper

c Why is the light scattered in all directions when it hits the paper?

Bicycles have reflectors. A reflector has an uneven surface to scatter the light in many directions. It also reflects a lot of light. This means that the cyclist can be seen clearly at night.

Mirrors

A mirror is smooth. Look at the diagram. All the light rays are reflected in the same direction. The light is not scattered. You can see your image in a mirror because the light is not scattered.

Light from a car's headlamps will be scattered by the bicycle's reflector.

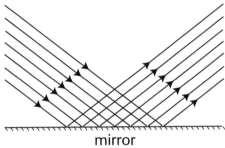

mirror

d Why can you see your image in a mirror, but not in a piece of paper?

The image in a mirror is the wrong way round. Left is right and right is left. This is why ambulances have the word ƎƆИA⅃UᗺMA on the front. Drivers can read it in their mirrors.

Using mirrors

You can use mirrors to see around corners, or over a wall. Look at the diagram. This periscope uses two mirrors so you can see what is happening above you.

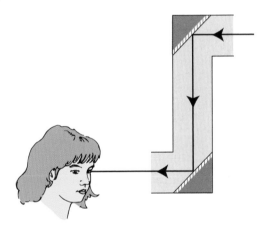

A periscope.

Questions

1 Copy and complete these sentences.

Light bounces off most surfaces. We say the light is _____.

Very smooth surfaces reflect the light in the same direction, so we see an _____.

Rough surfaces _____ the light.

2 Look at the diagram of a periscope above.

   a What is the angle between the incoming ray and the mirror?

   b What is the angle between the reflected ray and the mirror?

   c Explain how you can use a periscope to look over a wall.

3 A puddle can act as a mirror. Use a diagram to explain this.

For your notes:

- Light is **reflected** from many surfaces.

- The angle between the ray and the surface is the same for the incoming ray and reflected ray.

- Most surfaces **scatter** light when they reflect it.

- Mirrors do not scatter light because they are smooth.

K3 Travelling through?

Learn about:
- Absorption
- Transmission
- Refraction

Absorption or transmission?

Light is not always reflected when it hits a surface. When light hits **opaque** materials like wood or bricks, it is 'soaked up'. This is called **absorption**. The light energy is transferred into heat energy.

When light hits **transparent** materials like glass and water, it travels through them. We say the light is **transmitted**. Sometimes part of the light is absorbed and part is transmitted. Materials that both absorb and transmit light are called **translucent**. Thin paper is translucent.

A trick of the light

You sometimes see odd things when light goes through a transparent material like water or glass.

Light bends when it goes from air to water, or from glass to air. We call this bending **refraction**. Look at the photos. Refraction makes the pencil look bent, and the words look bigger.

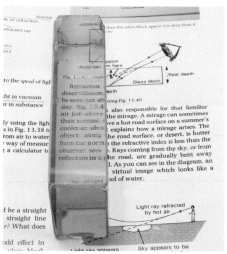

a Why does the pencil look bent?

Air to glass

Light **refracts** (bends) when it goes from air to glass. The path of the light bends inwards.

Look at diagram **A**. If the light enters glass straight (at 90°), the light does not bend. Look at diagrams **B** and **C**. When the ray of light hits the glass at an angle, it bends.

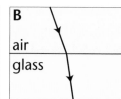
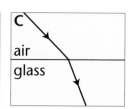

b Will the light bend when it hits the glass at:
   (i) 45°?   **(ii) 90°?**

Glass to air

The light also bends when it goes from glass to air. The path of the light bends outwards.

Again, if the ray hits straight on (at 90°), it does not bend.

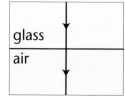
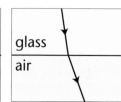
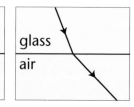

The glass block

When light goes through a glass block it goes from air to glass, then from glass to air. The light refracts when it goes from air to glass, then refracts again as it goes from glass to air.

Look at the photo. When the light goes from air to glass it bends inwards. When the light goes from glass to air it bends outwards. The light comes from **A**. It travels through the block and ends up at **B**.

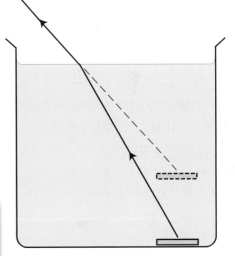

Water to air

Refraction also happens when light travels from water to air. Look at the diagram. Light from the coin is refracted when it goes from the water to the air.

Your brain thinks that light travels in straight lines. You see the coin higher up, where the light seems to come from.

c What happens when the light goes from the water to the air?

d The water above the coin seems shallower than it really is. Why does your brain think that the water is shallower?

Questions

1 Copy and complete the sentences using the words below.

transparent   opaque   absorbed   refraction   angle

Light is _____ by many materials.

When the light does not go through the material, we say the material is _____.

Light goes through _____ materials like water, air and glass. When the light enters a transparent material at an _____, it bends. This bending is called _____.

2 Which is the correct ray in each diagram, **A**, **B** or **C**?

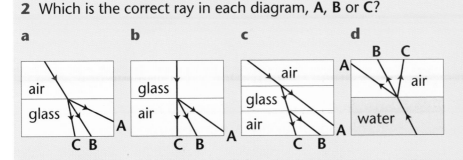

For your notes:

- Light is **absorbed** and/or **transmitted** by some materials. These materials can be **transparent**, **translucent** or **opaque**.

- When light goes from one transparent material to another, it may **refract** (bend).

- The light must enter the new material at an angle for refraction to happen.

K4 Coloured light

Splitting white light

You see a rainbow when sunlight goes through raindrops. The raindrops split the light into many colours.

You can get the same splitting into colours with a prism. This is shown in the photo.

We call the colours a **spectrum**. The splitting up is called **dispersion**. White light enters the prism and is separated into the colours of the spectrum. The colours are always in the same order: red, orange, yellow, green, blue, indigo and violet.

a What do we call:
(i) the 'rainbow' of colours made using a prism?
(ii) the splitting up of light?

You can mix the different colours together. Mixing the colours gives you white light. You can read more about this on page 118.

Coloured filters

Look at the photo of a stained glass window. Only red light comes through the red glass in the window. The red glass absorbs the other colours.

Did you know?

You can remember the colours of the spectrum like this:

Richard **O**f **Y**ork **G**ave **B**attle **I**n **V**ain.

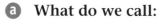

white light falls on the glass

green light comes through – other colours absorbed

red light comes through – other colours absorbed

blue light comes through – other colours absorbed

b What colour of light comes through the blue glass?

c Only green light comes through the green glass. What happens to the other colours in the light?

Seeing by reflection

A red surface reflects red light. The red light enters your eyes and you see red. If you shine white light onto a red surface, the red light is reflected and the other colours are absorbed.

d What colour of light is reflected by a blue surface?

e What happens to red light when it hits a blue surface?

Photographers develop their film in a darkroom. They use a special red light to see. The red light does not affect the film.

Things look odd inside a darkroom when the red light is on. The photographer in the picture is wearing a white shirt, but it looks red. This is because there is only red light in the room. The white shirt reflects all colours of light, so it reflects the red light.

f What is the only colour of light in the darkroom?

g What colour of light is being reflected from the shirt?

The photographer is wearing green trousers, but they look black. This is because there is no green light for the trousers to reflect.

h What happens to the red light when it hits the photographer's trousers?

Did you know?

Look at the spectrum. There are lots more than seven colours. Isaac Newton, the famous scientist, decided to name seven colours because he thought that the number 7 was magical!

Questions

1 Copy and complete the sentences using the words below.

absorbs   reflects   spectrum   dispersion

White light is made up of a _____ of seven different colours. We separate white light into colours by _____. A coloured filter _____ one colour of light and _____ all the others. A coloured surface _____ one colour of light and _____ all the others.

2 Conor is investigating light using coloured filters. He does the experiments shown below. What colours of light (if any) will he see at **A**, **B**, **C** and **D**?

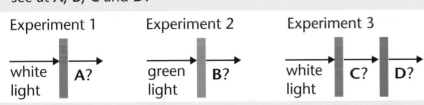

Experiment 1	Experiment 2	Experiment 3
white light → **A?**	green light → **B?**	white light → **C?** → **D?**

For your notes:

- White light can be split into a **spectrum** of different colours. This is called **dispersion**.

- A red, green or blue filter allows only one colour of light through and absorbs the others.

- A coloured object reflects the colour we see and absorbs the other colours.

Combinations

Joe collects copper coins for charity. He counts the money and puts it into bags. There are three possible **combinations**:

- 1p coins in a bag
- 2p coins in a bag
- a bag of 1p and 2p coins.

The coins can be combined in three different ways, to make three different combinations. You can read more about combinations in the blue box on page 119.

Primary colours of light

The photo shows a television screen close up. The screen is made up of red, green and blue dots.

Red, green and blue are the three **primary colours** of light. All colours of light can be made from combining these colours.

a How many different combinations of red, green and blue can you make?

Secondary colours

Secondary colours of light are made by mixing red, green and blue light. Look at the colour chart. It shows what happens when you combine red, green and blue light. For example, colour **E** is made by combining **A** with **C**.

b Copy this table and use the colour chart to fill in the gaps.

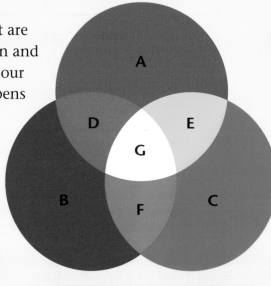

Lighting the show

Zahir wanted to help with lighting for the school play. Miss Lawrence set him a test about colour.

c Do the 'Lighting test'. It is in the green box on the page 119.

d Mark your answers (see the bottom of page 119).

Zahir could not do questions 6 and 7.

e Write down what you would say to explain questions 6 and 7 to Zahir. Draw any diagrams that you would use.

Position	Colour	Which combination of red, blue, green?
A	red	
B	blue	
C	green	
D	magenta	
E	yellow	
F	cyan	
G	white	

An example of combinations

Jane has bought some sweets. She has toffees, cream eggs and boiled sweets.
How many different combinations can she make?

Jane can have each type of sweet on its own:

 toffee  cream egg boiled sweet

Jane can have two types of sweets together: Jane can have all three types of sweets together:

So there are seven different types of combination.

Lighting test

Imagine you have only three spotlights: red, green and blue.

What combinations of red, green and blue do you use to make the following colours:

1 yellow?   **2** cyan?   **3** magenta?   **4** white?

You can change the colour of a spotlight by putting in different filters.

What combination of primary colours gets through each of the following filters
(*Remember:* only red, green and blue are primary colours):

5 red filter?   **6** yellow filter?   **7** cyan filter?

Questions

1 Bernie is putting up fairy lights to celebrate the New Year.
He has four different types of bulb that he can use:

- red flashing
- red
- green flashing
- green.

What different combinations of bulbs could Bernie put in his
string of fairy lights? List them all.

Answers to Lighting test

1 green and red
2 green and blue
3 red and blue
4 red, green and blue
5 red
6 red and green
7 blue and green

L1 Good vibrations

Making music

Some pupils investigate sound using a kettledrum.

a What part of the drum vibrates to make the sound?

You change the pitch by changing the tension in the drum skin. A tighter skin gives a higher pitch, a looser skin gives a lower pitch.

I think pitch is to do with how fast the skin vibrates.

You change the loudness by hitting the drum differently. Hitting it harder gives a louder sound.

I think loudness is to do with how big the vibrations are.

Testing their ideas

Their teacher says that they can test their ideas using a **microphone** and a **cathode ray oscilloscope**, or **CRO**. The microphone turns the sound into an electrical signal. The CRO then shows the electrical signal on the screen.

b What does the microphone do to the sound?

c What does the CRO let the pupils see?

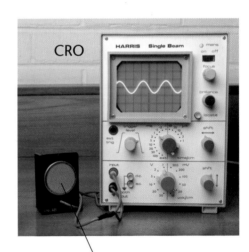

CRO

microphone

Pitch

The pupils then use tuning forks to make sounds with different pitches. They observe the electrical signals on the screen of the CRO. Look at the top diagram on the next page.

Jon makes a low-pitched sound using a tuning fork. The orange line shows the pattern on the screen of the CRO.

Letticia then makes a high-pitched sound with a tuning fork. The purple line shows the CRO pattern for her sound.

The size of the vibrations is the same. The number of vibrations in the time shown is different. The lower-pitched sound shows two vibrations. The higher-pitched sound shows four vibrations. The higher-pitched sound has more vibrations in the same time: it is faster. Faster vibrations make higher-pitched sounds.

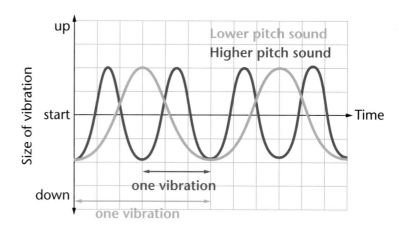

d **What is the difference in CRO pattern between the higher-pitched sound and the lower-pitched sound?**

Loudness

The pupils then make three notes of the same pitch but with different loudness. The graph shows the three patterns from the CRO.

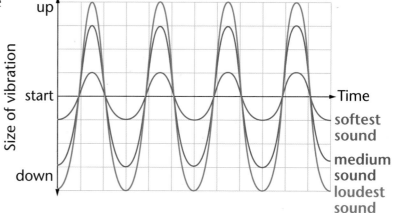

e **In what way are the three sounds the same?**

f **In what way are the three sounds different?**

Bigger vibrations make louder sounds. Smaller vibrations make softer sounds.

Questions

1 Look at 'For your notes'. Copy and complete these sentences.

Sounds are made by things that _____. Pitch is how _____ or _____ a sound is. _____ vibrations give higher-pitched sounds. Loudness is how _____ or _____ a sound is. Bigger vibrations give _____ sounds.

2 Compare sounds B to F with sound A.

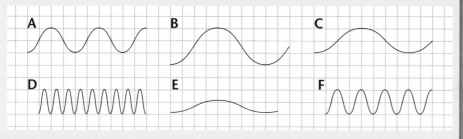

a Which sounds are **(i)** louder than A? **(ii)** softer than A?
(iii) the same loudness as A?

b Which sounds are **(i)** higher-pitched than A?
(ii) lower-pitched than A?

For your notes:

- Sound is made when something **vibrates**.

- Faster vibrations make sounds with a higher **pitch**. Slower vibrations make lower-pitched sounds.

- Bigger vibrations make louder sounds. Smaller vibrations make softer sounds.

- A **CRO** shows the pattern of sounds on a screen.

L2 Passing through

Materials

Harry's class is thinking about the materials that sound can travel through.

Sound can travel through solids, liquids and gases.

a **Look at the pictures above. What two pieces of evidence suggest that sound can travel through a solid?**

No material

A famous scientist called Robert Boyle was very interested in air. He knew that sound travelled through air and he wanted to know if sound needed air to travel.

At last! A good enough pump to get rid of all the air in my jar.

JANUARY
1657

DAILY TRIBUNE
NEW PUMP INVENTED

When I turn the handle the striker hits the bell. You hear the sound of the bell.

Now I have pumped all the air out of the jar. I am turning the handle. Can anyone hear the bell?

No!

How amazing!

b **What do you think happened when Robert Boyle let the air back into the jar and the striker hit the bell?**

Robert Boyle showed that sound needs a material to travel through. It isn't like light, which can travel through empty space between the Sun and the Earth.

Different materials

Sound travels faster in some materials and slower in others. Jon and Harry look up the speed of sound in six different materials. They present the data in a table.

Jon says that sound travels slower in gases than in solids or liquids.

Material	Description	Speed of sound in m/s
air	gas	330
helium	gas	972
water	liquid	1500
oil	liquid	1326
wood (oak)	solid	3850
iron	solid	5000

c What other information should Jon collect to check his conclusion?

d Railway tracks 'sing' or vibrate long before you can hear a train coming. Use the data in the table to explain why.

Light overtakes sound

Ayesha wants to compare the speed of sound in air with the speed of light in air. She looks up the speed of light. Light travels at 300 million m/s. Light travels almost a million times faster than sound.

e Lightning and thunder are made at the same time in a storm. Explain why you often see lightning before you hear the thunder.

For your notes:

- Sound needs a **material** to travel through.

- Sound travels through different materials at different speeds.

- Sound travels much more slowly than light.

Questions

1 Match the beginnings and ends to make sentences.

Beginning	End
Sound can travel through …	… a vacuum.
Sound travels much slower …	… solids, liquids and gases.
Sound cannot travel through …	… than light.

2 Oil is piped thousands of miles using pipelines. Sometimes the pipelines get blocked by air. It is difficult to find the blockage without looking inside every section of pipe. Instead scientists measure the speed of sound in the pipe.

a Use the table above to answer this question.
What is the speed of sound in:
(i) air? **(ii)** oil?

b Will sound travel faster or slower in the section of pipe that contains air?

c Why is this method of finding the blockage better than opening each section of pipe?

Learn about:
- How ears hear
- Different people's hearing

How do we hear sounds?

We hear sounds with our ears. Look at the drawing of the ear. When a sound reaches our ears, the eardrum vibrates.

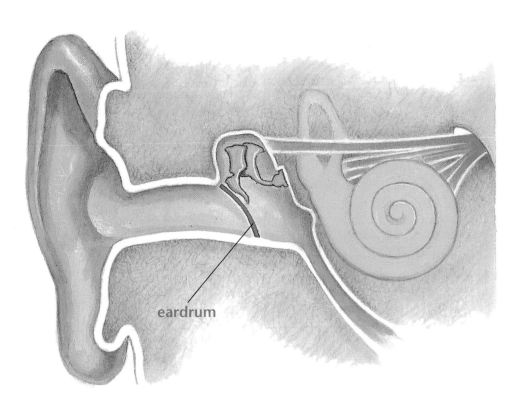

eardrum

ⓐ What happens to the eardrum when the sound reaches it?

When the eardrum vibrates, it makes some small bones vibrate.

The inner ear changes the vibrations into electrical signals. These electrical signals go through the nerves to the brain.

ⓑ How does the electrical signal get to your brain?

Your ear transfers the energy from the sound to your brain.

Is it working?

Look at the photo. It shows the eardrum. The eardrum must vibrate for us to hear.

ⓒ What will happen if the eardrum breaks?

The eardrum can break if the ear is badly infected, or hit very hard. This means that the vibrations are not passed on. Most broken eardrums can heal themselves.

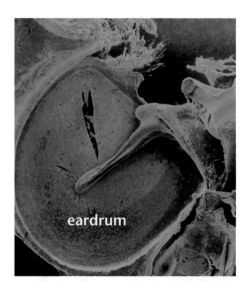

eardrum

Inside an ear.

What sounds do we hear?

The man in the photo is using a dog whistle. Dogs can hear the whistle but humans cannot. This is because dogs can hear higher-pitched sounds than humans.

Look at the bar chart. It shows the range of pitch that some different mammals can hear. We measure pitch in **kilohertz**. High-pitched sounds have more kilohertz.

You can see that dogs can hear sounds up to 45 kilohertz. Humans can hear sounds only up to 23 kilohertz. The chart also shows that a person's hearing changes with age.

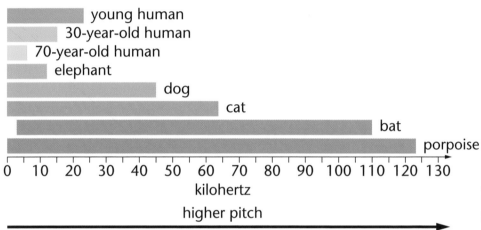

The bars show the range of pitch that can be heard.

d Look at the bar chart. Which animal hears sounds with the largest range of pitch?

e Use the chart to describe how humans' hearing changes as we get older.

Questions

1 Put these events in the correct order to explain how we hear.

   A The inner ear makes the vibrations into an electrical signal.
   B The sound makes the eardrum vibrate.
   C The electrical signal goes along the nerves to the brain.
   D The eardrum makes the small bones vibrate.

2 Look at the bar chart showing the hearing ranges of different animals.

   a Is the chart about the pitch of sounds or the loudness of sounds?
   b Which animal cannot hear some low-pitched sounds?
   c Which animal hears the narrowest range of sounds, humans or elephants? Explain how you decided on your answer.

For your notes:

● The **eardrum** vibrates when sound enters the ear.

● Some sounds are too high-pitched or too low-pitched for humans to hear.

● As humans get older, they are unable to hear high-pitched sounds.

Living with noise

Look at the photos. They show people who work where the sound is very loud. We call the sound from the chainsaw '**noise**' because it is sound no-one wants. We call the sound in the nightclub 'music'. People enjoy listening to music. Whether it is music or noise, loud sounds can damage your hearing.

We measure loudness with a sound meter. Loudness is measured in **decibels**. A very quiet whisper may be 1 decibel. A loud sound like a vacuum cleaner is 70 decibels. A jet plane overhead is about 100 decibels.

Bang!

Very, very loud sounds, like those made by an explosion, can break the eardrum. Too much energy is passed to the eardrum so it stretches and breaks. Sounds of over 120 decibels can damage the eardrum.

a **Why does breaking the eardrum stop the ear working?**

Too loud

Very loud sounds of 90 to 110 decibels also cause **hearing impairment**. After going to a nightclub, the clubbers may not hear very well. Normal sounds seem quiet. They may ask people to speak up. Their ears have become numb. The numbness wears off quite quickly. By next morning their ears will work again.

We measure loudness with a sound meter.

If this happens again and again, the numbness may become permanent. People who work with very loud noises every day are in danger of damaging their hearing. That is why the man with the chainsaw is wearing ear protectors. It is why some rock stars and DJs lose their hearing as they get older.

ⓑ **Music in some clubs is played at about 110 decibels.**
  (i) **What is the danger to people who come to the club once a week?**
  (ii) **What is the danger to the DJ who works there every night?**

There are very strict regulations about loud sounds. Employers have to cut down the noise as much as they can. They also have to provide ear protectors.

Loud sounds may damage the inner ear, or the nerves that carry the signals from the inner ear to the brain.

Cutting noise

Noise can cause irritation and stress even if it is not loud enough to damage people's hearing. **Sound insulation** lets people make the noise they want without annoying others. Lining a room with sound insulation materials 'soaks up' the sound vibrations. This means the vibrations do not cause sound outside the room. Rubber and foam make good sound insulation.

ⓒ **Mary's parents are thinking about taking away her drum kit. What could Mary do to cut down the noise?**

Questions

1 How loud does sound have to be to:
  a break the eardrum?
  b cause 'numbing' of the ear?

2 Suggest some materials to put in ear protectors as sound insulation.

3 Match the sound with the correct number of decibels.

loud thunderclap	busy street	chatting	whispering
60	3	70	110

For your notes:

- Very, very loud sounds can break the eardrum and stop the ear working.

- Loud sounds can cause **hearing impairment**. If they go on for a long time, this can be permanent.

- **Sound insulation** 'soaks up' the vibrations, stopping the sound.

L5 Detect it

Senses

There are five senses: sight, hearing, touch, smell and taste. We use our senses to collect information about our surroundings. Compared with other animals, humans' best sense is probably sight. We see in colour. We are good at seeing movement. We can judge distance.

Scientists need to collect information. Although their senses are good, they are sometimes not good enough. They invent special equipment to extend their senses.

a **Using your general knowledge, what scientific equipment do scientists use to detect:**
(i) **things that are too small to see?**
(ii) **things that are too far away to see?**

Seeing the sound

There are many sounds that humans cannot hear. We use a microphone and a CRO to see sounds we can't hear.

b **Graph A shows the pattern on a CRO for a 1000 kilohertz sound.**
(i) **How many vibrations are shown?**
(ii) **Would there be more or fewer vibrations for lower-pitched sound? (*Hint:* Check back to page 121 if you are not sure.)**
(iii) **Look at graph B. Which pattern shows the 200 kilohertz sound?**
(iv) **Look at graph B. Which pattern shows the 2000 kilohertz sound?**
(v) **Look at graphs A and B. What is the same for all three sounds? What does this tell us?**

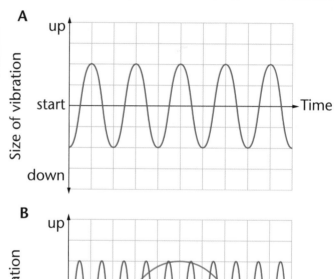

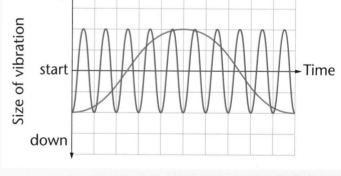

Seeing the heat

We can detect heat energy, but only when the hot object is very close to our skin, or it is very, very hot (like the Sun).

We use an infrared camera to see heat energy at a distance. The camera changes the heat energy into light for us to see.

c **Suggest a use for infrared cameras. (*Hint:* Look on page 96.)**

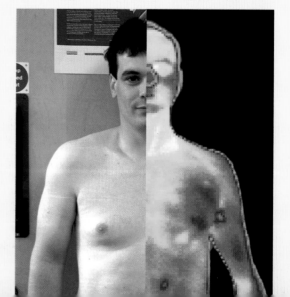

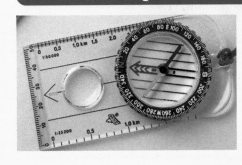

Other instruments

Scientists have invented other special equipment. Two scientific instruments are shown in the photos.

The compass detects the magnetic field by pointing towards north. We cannot detect a magnetic field without it, but pigeons can!

The chromatography machine is more sensitive than a dog's nose. It detects tiny amounts of chemicals in the air. It shows the information as a chart that we can see.

d **Why do you think much scientific equipment changes information into something we can see?**

Questions

1 Which scientific instrument would you choose to do each task in the table? Match the task with the correct scientific instrument. Use the information on these pages and your knowledge of science.

Task	Scientific instrument
finding the direction of a magnetic field	ammeter
seeing things that are far away	universal indicator paper
detecting a sound that is too high-pitched to hear	compass
measuring an electric current	chromatography machine
detecting chemicals we cannot smell or taste	thermometer
measuring acidity	telescope
detecting heat energy at a distance	microscope
measuring temperature	CRO
seeing things which are very small	infrared camera

2 Dogs can see in dimmer light than humans. They see movement better than humans. Everything at a distance is blurred to a dog. They see yellow and blue but not red and green – red and green probably look grey to a dog. Most dogs' eyes are about 30 cm from the floor. Draw a picture of what the world might look like to a dog.

3 Many scientific instruments take in information about the environment and change it into light energy, so we can see it. Imagine if dogs became scientists. Do you think they would make scientific instruments that gave out **a** light energy, **b** sound energy or **c** chemicals that they could smell? Give reasons for your choice.

Glossary

absorbed/absorption The process by which digested food passes through the lining of the small intestine into the blood.

When light or sound is soaked up by a surface, it is absorbed.

adaptations Having features that help a living thing to survive in a particular place.

aerobic respiration The process by which plants and animals use oxygen from the air to break down their food to release the chemical energy from it.

agar plate A plate containing agar jelly used by scientists to grow bacteria.

air resistance The friction a moving object makes with air.

alveoli Tiny, thin-walled air sacs in the lungs.

anorexia nervosa An eating disorder which causes a person to eat too little.

antibiotic A medicine that kills bacteria but has no effect on viruses.

antibodies Special chemicals, produced by white blood cells, which attach themselves to the outside of microbes and kill them.

antiseptics Chemicals that kill bacteria.

anus The opening through which undigested food passes out of the body.

arteries Blood vessels in which blood flows away from the heart.

atom The simplest type of particle.

attracts Pulling force between magnets and some metals.

bacteria Unicellular microbes with a cell wall but no nucleus.

balanced diet A diet that has the right amounts of all the nutrients.

balanced forces Two forces of the same size pulling in opposite directions.

bar magnet A rectangular magnet.

basalt A type of igneous rock with small crystals.

blood vessels Tubes in which blood flows all around the body.

boiling point The temperature at which a liquid element becomes a gas.

breathe The process of getting air in and out of our lungs.

°C The short way to write degrees Celsius.

calcium A mineral found in milk and cheese, and it keeps your teeth and bones healthy. The mineral calcium is actually calcium compounds.

capillaries Very small blood vessels.

carbohydrates Nutrients found in foods such as bread, which give you energy.

carbon dioxide A waste product of respiration. A gas that is produced when carbon burns and joins with oxygen.

cathode ray oscilloscope (CRO) Machine that shows the pattern of sound on a screen.

cells Tiny building blocks that make up all living things.

cell membrane A thin layer that surrounds the cell and controls the movement of substances in and out of the cell.

cell wall A tough box-like wall around plant cells.

Celsius A temperature scale in which 0 °C represents freezing water and 100 °C represents boiling water.

cementation In the gaps between compacted grains in sedimentary layers, chemicals in the water crystallise and 'glue' the grains together.

changes of state Changing from a solid to a liquid or a liquid to a gas and back again – melting, freezing, boiling, condensing.

chemical energy Energy stored in a material, which will be given out in a chemical reaction.

chemical weathering The breaking up of rocks by chemicals in the environment. The substances in the rocks are changed into new substances.

chlorophyll A green substance that is needed for photosynthesis.

chloroplasts The parts of a plant cell that carry out photosynthesis.

combinations Ways in which objects are put together.

compaction Grains in sedimentary layers pressed tightly together by the enormous weight of layers of sediment deposited later.

compass Instrument used for navigation, with a magnetic needle which points to the Earth's North Pole unless there is a magnet close by.

competition The struggle between organisms in a habitat for scarce resources, eg food, water, space.

compound A substance with more than one type of atom joined together.

conduction Thermal energy is passed from particle to particle in a solid.

cones In plants – structures that contain the seeds in conifers.

conifers Plants that reproduce from seeds in cones and have thin, needle-like leaves.

constipated Difficulty in emptying the bowels.

consumer An animal, that eats (consumes) plants or other animals.

contract A material getting smaller.

control A second experiment where the variable being investigated in the first experiment is held constant.

convection Particles move, transferring thermal energy from particle to particle.

convection current A circular movement of hot gas (or liquid) rising and cool gas (or liquid) falling.

core Magnetic material placed inside a coil of wire (with an electric current running through it), to make the magnetic field stronger.

correlation A link between two or more things.

CRO Cathode ray oscilloscope.

crystals Groups of molecules with a symmetrical structure.

cuticle A waterproof layer on the surface of some leaves.

cytoplasm A jelly-like substance found inside cells.

decibels A measurement for the loudness of sound.

decomposers An organism that feeds on the dead bodies of plants and animals.

degrees Celsius A temperature scale in which 0 °C represents freezing water and 100 °C represents boiling water.

delta New land formed by deposition at the mouth of a river.

dense A dense material has a lot of particles in a small volume.

deposition Small pieces of rock settling at the bottom of a river or the sea.

digestion Process by which food is broken down into smaller molecules.

digestive system The organ system that breaks down your food into smaller molecules and absorbs them.

dispersion The splitting of white light into colours.

eardrum Part of the ear that vibrates when sound reaches it.

ecosystem An area such as a forest or a pond, including all the living things in it and also its soil, air and climate.

egestion Passing undigested food out of the body.

electrical energy Energy carried by electricity.

electromagnet A magnet that can be switched on and off using electricity.

element A substance that cannot be broken down into anything simpler.

energy Energy makes things work. When anything happens, energy is transferred.

environment The surroundings in a habitat.

enzymes Proteins that speed up the breakdown of food in digestion.

erosion Loose pieces of rock are broken down while being transported.

evaporating/evaporation The change of a liquid into a gas using thermal energy transferred from the liquid's surroundings.

expand A material getting bigger.

faeces The undigested food that is egested from the body.

fats Nutrients found in foods, such as butter, that give you energy and insulate your body.

ferns Plants that reproduce from spores and have leaves called fronds.

fibre Bulky material found in cereals, fruits and vegetables that helps to keep food moving through your gut.

flowering plants Plants that reproduce from seeds made in flowers and have various shapes of leaf.

food chain A diagram that shows how the organisms in an ecosystem feed on each other.

food web Lots of food chains linked together to show the feeding relationships in an ecosystem.

force An action on something that causes it to move, change direction or change shape.

formula Symbols used to represent atoms in a compound.

fossils The remains of animals or plants that have been buried deep underground for millions of years and preserved.

friction The force that is made when things rub together.

fronds The large tough leaves of ferns.

fungi (*singular* **fungus**) Living things that feed on rotting material, for example toadstools.

gas exchange In alveoli, the movement of oxygen into the blood and carbon dioxide out of the blood.

geologists Scientists who study the Earth and rocks.

glucose A small molecule formed by breaking down carbohydrates, or made by plants in photosynthesis.

grains Tiny pieces of material, such as sand.

granite A type of igneous rock with big crystals.

gravitational energy Energy stored because something is lifted up.

groups The eight vertical columns in the periodic table.

gut The long tube in your body down which food passes between the mouth and the anus, and where digestion and absorption take place.

habitat A place where an organism lives, that provides all the things the organism needs to carry out the life processes.

hearing impairment Damaged hearing.

heat energy Energy transferred from a hot object to a cooler object.

humus Dead animal and plant material found in soil. It provides plants with nutrients.

hydrogen peroxide A compound containing two hydrogen and two oxygen atoms.

hypothesis A possible explanation for why something happens.

igneous rock Rock that is formed from molten lava or magma that has cooled and solidified.

image An object seen indirectly on a screen or using a mirror or lens.

immune Protected against infection.

immune system The body's defences against infection.

immunised Protected against a disease caused by microbes.

infections Diseases.

infrared radiation Carries thermal energy from a hotter object to a cooler object.

interdependent Dependent on each other.

interdependence Organisms in the same food web all depend on each other.

interlocking Crystals in rocks which fit together with no gaps between them are interlocking.

iron filings Tiny shavings of iron used to show a magnet's magnetic field.

J The short way of writing joules.

joules Energy is measured in joules.

key A set of questions to help us classify things

key variables Variables that will have a large effect in an investigation.

kilohertz A measurement for pitch or frequency. 1000 hertz.

kilojoules There are 1000 joules in 1 kilojoule.

kJ The short way of writing kilojoules.

large intestine The part of the gut where waste food is stored and water is absorbed.

lateral thinking Thinking in a different direction.

lava Molten rock from deep below the surface of the Earth that reaches the surface through cracks or volcanoes.

light energy Energy transferred by light.

light sensors Equipment used to detect light.

limestone A type of sedimentary rock formed from the shells and bones of sea creatures, which contains calcium carbonate.

line of best fit A line drawn on a graph that shows the overall trend or pattern.

lodestone Iron oxide, a natural magnet.

magma Molten rock found deep below the surface of the Earth.

magnetic Attracted to a magnet.

magnetic field The space around a magnet where it attracts and repels.

magnetic field lines The magnetic field around a magnet. Magnetic field lines run from the north pole of a magnet to its south pole.

magnetic materials Materials that are attracted to a magnet.

marble A type of metamorphic rock that is produced when limestone is heated under high pressure.

material A solid, liquid or a gas, not empty space. Sound needs matter to travel through.

melting point The temperature at which a solid element becomes a liquid.

metals Materials that are usually solid and shiny when polished. A few are magnetic.

metamorphic rock Rock formed when sedimentary or igneous rocks are changed by intense heat and/or pressure.

MgO The formula representing magnesium oxide.

microbes Another name for microorganisms.

microorganism A very small living thing that can only be seen with a microscope.

microphone Equipment that turns sound into an electrical signal.

minerals All rocks are made up of compounds called minerals. Different rocks are made up of different minerals or different mixtures of minerals.

Compounds of calcium, iron, iodine and other elements, that are needed in the diet in small amounts to keep your body healthy, are also called minerals.

mixture A material that contains more than one substance.

molecule A group of atoms joined together.

mosses Small plants that look like a springy cushion. They reproduce from spores and have very small leaves.

N The short way of writing newtons.

navigate To plan directions to find the way.

negative correlation When two variables move in opposite directions.

newtons Force is measured in newtons.

noise Sound.

non-interlocking Round grains in rocks which do not fit together, as there are gaps between them, are non-interlocking.

non-metals Materials that are usually solids or gases. They have many different appearances.

north pole One end of a magnet. It attracts the south pole of another magnet.

nucleus The part of a cell that controls everything the cell does.

nutrients Useful substances present in foods.

obese People who are very overweight for their height are obese.

opaque A material that does not allow light to pass through, but absorbs it, is opaque.

organ A group of different tissues that work together to do a job.

oxygen A non-metallic element that is a gas. Oxygen is used in burning and in respiration.

particle An atom or a molecule.

particle model The idea that everything is made up of particles.

pathogens Organisms that cause disease.

periodic table A table containing all 113 elements, arranged by their properties into groups (columns) and periods (rows).

periods The seven horizontal rows in the periodic table.

permanent magnet A material that stays as a magnet for many years.

physical weathering Breaking down rocks into smaller pieces, without changing them into new substances. Physical weathering can be caused by water, wind and changes in temperature.

pinhole camera The simplest type of camera – a box with a pinhole at one end and a screen at the other.

pitch Sounds can have a high or low pitch. Faster vibrations make higher-pitched sounds than slower vibrations.

placebo 'Medicine' that does not contain any medicine.

poles The two different ends of a magnet.

pond dipping A technique to find out what organisms live in different parts of a pond.

population The number of organisms of a particular species living in a habitat.

porous A substance such as a rock with lots of tiny holes in it is porous.

positive correlation When two variables move in the same direction.

precipitate A solid made when two liquids react.

predicting To state before something happens what might happen.

primary colour One of three colours of light that humans can see – green, red or blue.

producer A plant, that produces its own food by photosynthesis.

products The new substances that are formed in chemical reactions.

properties The appearance of a material and the way it reacts.

proteins Nutrients found in foods such as fish, used in your body for growth and repair.

pure A material that contains only one substance.

pyramid of numbers A drawing of the number of organisms at each level of a food chain.

quadrat A wooden frame measuring one metre on all four sides.

radiation The transfer of thermal energy without particles.

random samples Taking samples from different places without choosing the places deliberately.

ratio A way of showing a scale factor. For example, a scale of 1:10 means you have to multiply your number or measurement by 10 to get the real measurement.

ray A thin beam of light.

reactants The substances that take part in a chemical reaction, that change into the products.

reflection/reflects When light or sound bounces off a surface, it is reflected.

refraction/refracts Bending of light when it travels from one material to another, eg air to water or glass to air.

repel Pushing away force between magnets and magnetic materials.

reproduce To make more organisms of the same species.

respiration The process by which plants and animals break down their food to release the chemical energy from it.

rickets A disease caused by not eating enough vitamin D in the diet, in which the bones are soft.

rock cycle A cycle that describes how the three rock types change from one to another over millions of years.

sandstone A type of sedimentary rock made up of grains of sand cemented together.

scatter When light is reflected in many directions by a rough surface, it is scattered.

scurvy A disease caused by not eating enough vitamin C in the diet, in which the gums bleed and the skin does not heal.

sediment Small pieces of rock and dead living things which build up in layers at the bottoms of lakes or seas over millions of years.

sedimentary layers Layers of sediment that have built up over millions of years and become cemented together into rock.

sedimentary rocks A type of rock made up from layers of sediment that have built up over millions of years and become cemented together.

sexually transmitted diseases Diseases that can be caught from sexual intercourse without protection.

sound energy Energy transferred by sound.

sound insulation Material that 'soaks up' sound vibrations and stops sound, eg rubber and foam.

source Where something starts or is produced.

south pole One end of a magnet. It attracts the north pole of another magnet.

spectrum The colours in white light – red, orange, yellow, green, blue, indigo, violet.

spores Structures used for reproduction in mosses and ferns.

states of matter The three states of matter are solid, liquid and gas.

store Keep something for later use.

strain energy Energy stored in a material because the material is being pulled or pushed.

symbol Sign representing an element, eg Fe is the symbol for iron.

temperature The energy per particle measured in degrees Celsius.

temporary magnet A material that only acts as a magnet when it is in a magnetic field.

texture The feel or appearance of a material.

thermal conductor A material that conducts thermal energy well.

thermal energy The scientific name for heat energy.

thermal insulator A material that conducts thermal energy poorly.

tissue A group of similar cells that carry out the same job.

topsoil The top layer of soil, made of tiny grains of rock and humus.

transferred Moved from one place to another.

translucent A material which both absorbs and transmits light is translucent.

transmitted When light or sound passes through a material, it is transmitted.

transparent A material that allows (transmits) light through is transparent.

unbalanced forces Forces pushing in different directions where one force is bigger than the other. An unbalanced force makes the object move or speed up or slow down.

upthrust The force caused by water pushing up against an object.

vaccination An injection of dead or inactive microbes into your body to make you immune to a disease before you catch it.

vacuole A bag inside plant cells that contains a liquid which keeps the cell firm.

vacuum A place where there are no particles.

veins In animals – a blood vessel in which blood flows towards the heart.

In plants – a tube-like structure that carries water, mineral salts and food around the plant.

vibrates Moves rapidly to and fro. Sound is made when something vibrates.

villi (*singular* **villus**) Finger-like structures in the small intestine which increase the area for the absorption of digested food.

viruses Microbes that are smaller than bacteria. They are not made of cells.

vitamin A substance, such as vitamin C, that is needed in the diet in very small amounts to keep your body healthy.

vitamin C A vitamin found in fresh fruit and vegetables.

water A compound of hydrogen and oxygen. Water is the solvent in which all the chemical reactions in your body take place.

weathering Breaking rock down by chemical or physical processes.

weight The force of gravitational attraction on an object, that makes it feel heavy.

white blood cells A vital part of the immune system, these blood cells help fight against microbes.

Index

Note: page numbers in **bold** are for glossary definitions

absorbed/absorption 10-11, 114, **130**
acid 28, 82
adaptations 38, **130**
aerobic respiration 15, **130**
agar plate 29, **130**
age and hearing loss 125
air
    gases in 62–3
    microbes in 26
    resistance x, **130**
    respiration and 14, 16, 18
    sound travels through 122–3
    see also breathing
aluminium 52, 53
    heat energy and 88, 98–9
aluminium chloride 65
alveoli 18–19, **130**
amylase 12
animals
    bites cause diseases 26
    competition 42–3
    in food web 41
    sounds heard by 125
    see also birds
Anning, Mary 74
anorexia nervosa 5, **130**
antibiotics 25, 29, **130**
antibodies 27, **130**
antiseptics 28, **130**
anus 8, 11, **130**
argon 62
Aristotle 21
arteries 20, 21, **130**
athlete's foot 26
atoms 47, 64, **130**
attracts 100, **130**

bacteria 24, **130**
    diseases and 26, 29, 33
    killing 28–9, 33
    useful 25
balanced diet 4–5, **130**
balanced forces x, **130**
bar magnet 101, **130**
    Earth as 102–3
barnacles 39
basalt 78, 81, 83, **130**
bats, hearing of 125

beach 39, 40
Beaumont, Dr William 9
biological washing powders 9
birds xi, 41, 93
blood
    cells, white 27, **138**
    flow/circulation 10, 19, 20–1
    vessels *see* arteries; capillaries; veins
bloodworm 39
boiling/boiling point 51, 57, **130**
    energy and 90, 91
    of gases in air 62–3
    heat energy and 84
Boyle, Robert 122
brain and sound 124
breathing/breathe 18–19, **130**
brewing 22
bromine 50, 52, 53

°C *see* Celsius
calcium 3, 48, **130**
calcium carbonate 68, 76–7
calcium chloride 64
calcium oxide 65
camera
    film 111
    infrared 96, 128
    pinhole 110, **136**
capillaries 21, **130**
carbohydrates 2, 4, 14, **130**
carbolic acid 28
carbon 51, 52, 62
carbon dioxide **130**
    in air 62
    from carbon and oxygen 51
    in rain 68
    respiration and 14, 16, 18, 19, 20
carnivore 40, 41
cathode ray oscilloscope (CRO) 120–1, 128, **130**
cats, hearing of 125
cautious thinking 75
cells ix, **131**
    chemical reactions in 59
    membrane ix, **131**
    plant ix
    wall ix, **131**
Celsius, Anders 84
Celsius (°C) 84, **131**

cementation 76, 80, **131**
cereal bars 6–7
changes of state **131**
  see also boiling; condensing; freezing; melting
chemical energy viii, **131**
chemical reactions 51, 54–5, 58–9
chemical weathering 68–9, **131**
chlorides 64, 65
  see also sodium chloride
chlorine 52, 57
  appearance of 50
  bacteria killed by 28, 33
  fact file 53
chlorophyll ix, **131**
chloroplasts ix, **131**
cholera 33
chromatography 60, 129
cleaning products 28
cobalt 48, 51, 100
coil of electromagnet 106–7
coldest place in solar system 84
colours 116–17
  primary 118–19, **136**
combinations 118–19, **131**
compaction 76, 80, **131**
compass 102, 103, 129, **131**
  making 104–5
competition 42–3, **131**
compounds 54–5, 56–9, 61, **131**
  chemical reactions 58–9
condensing 90
  point 84
conduction/conductors **131**
  electrical 51, 52
  thermal 92–3, **137**
cones 36, **131**
conifers 36, **131**
constipated 3, **131**
constructive thinking 75
consumer xi, **131**
contraction 67, 88–9, **131**
control 34, 35, **131**
convection current 94–5, **131**
cooling 67, 79, 90
copper 52, 58
  fact file 53
  heat energy and 98–9
  symbol for 48
copper oxide 55, 58
core of electromagnet 106–7, **131**
correlation 34–5, **131**

negative 34, 35, **135**
positive 34, 35, **136**
counting plants 44–5
cowpox 31
crabs 40, 41
cracking rocks 67
CRO (cathode ray oscilloscope) 120–1, 128, **132**
crystals 66, **132**
  in rock 66, 78, 82
cuticle 36, 37, **132**
cytoplasm ix, **132**

dead bodies 41
decibels 126–7, **132**
decomposers 41, **132**
defence systems 26–7
degrees Celsius *see* Celsius
delta 71, **132**
dense **132**
dependent variables 108–9
deposition 71–3, 80, **132**
deserts 67
diet *see* food
digestion 10, **132**
  digestive system 8–9, **132**
  of starch 9, 12–13
diseases
  cholera 33
  food and 3, 5, 6
  microbes and 26–7
  plague 32
  preventing 30–1
  scurvy 3, **137**
  sexually transmitted 26, **137**
  treating *see* medicines
  see also infections; medical care
dispersion 116, **132**
distillation 60–1
doctors *see* medical care
dogs, hearing of 125
drum 120–1

ear
  eardrum 124, **132**
  inner 127
  see also hearing
Earth's magnetic field 102–3
ecological relationships 36–45
  ecosystem 38–9
  food chain and web 40, 41
  populations 42–3

sampling 44–5
see also animals; habitat; plants
ecosystem 38–9, **132**
egestion 11, **132**
electrical energy viii, 106–7, **132**
    metals conducting 51, 52
    transferring sound to brain 124
electromagnets 106–9, **132**
elements 46–55, **132**
    burning 54
    chemical reactions 51, 54–5
    differences between 50–1
    mixtures of 46, 47, 62–3
    new substances from *see* compounds
    see also periodic table
elephant, hearing of 125
energy viii, **132**
    chemical viii, **131**
    electrical 106–7, **132**
    flow xi
    food for 2, 4, 14
    see also respiration
    gravitational viii, **133**
    per particle *see* temperature
    storage viii
    strain viii, **137**
    thermal *see* heat energy
    see also electrical; heat; light; sound
energy transfer viii, 124, **132**
    in food chain/web 40, 41
    sound 124
    see also conduction; convection; radiation
environment 38, **132**
enzymes and digestion 8–9, **132**
erosion 70–1, 73, 80, **132**
    see also weathering
ethanol 84
evaporation/evaporating 60, 96, **132**
exercise 15
expansion/expand 67, 88–9, **132**
explosion, noise of 126
Eyam and plague 32
eyes *see* seeing

faeces 11, **132**
fats in food 2, 14, **132**
    too many 5, 6
ferns 37, **132**
fibre 3, 11, **132**
filters, coloured 116

filtration 60
fish, fossil 74
fleas and disease 32
Fleming, Alexander 29
flowering plants 36, **133**
food 2–13
    absorption 10–11
    bacteria removed from 28
    bacteria used to make 25
    balanced diet 4–5, **130**
    butterfly xi
    chains xi, 40, 41, **133**
    competition for 43
    in different countries 5
    digestion 8–9
    for energy 2, 4, 14
    see also respiration
    for plants 16
    fungi used to make 25
    minerals in 3, 10, **135**
    nutrients 2, **135**
    webs xi, 41, **133**
forces x, **133**
    balanced x, **130**
    unbalanced x, **138**
forests *see* trees
formula 55, 64, **133**
fossils 72–3, 74, 76, 81, **133**
freezing 67, 90
friction x, **133**
fronds 37, **133**
fruit in diet 5
fungi/fungus 24, 25, 26, **133**
    yeast 22–3, 24, 25

gall bladder 8
gas/gases 50–1
    in air 62–3
    appearance of 50, 57
    exchange 19, **133**
    heat energy and 89, 91
        becoming liquids *see* condensing
        conduction 92
        contraction 89
        convection 94–5, **131**
        liquids becoming *see* boiling; evaporation
    particles in ix
    sound travels through 122–3
    see also carbon dioxide; chlorine; helium;
        hydrogen; nitrogen; oxygen

geologists 73, **133**
germs 24
   see also microbes
Gilbert, William 102
glass 114–15
glucose 9, 14, 20, **133**
gold 46, 47, 48
grains 66, 76, 82, **133**
Grand Canyon 73
granite 66, 69, 78, 81, **133**
graphs of starch digestion 12–13
gravitational energy viii, **133**
green hairstreak butterfly xi
groups in periodic table 48–9, **133**
gullet (oesophagus) 8
gut 8, **133**

habitat 37–45, **133**
   competition for 42–3
   different types of 38–9
   ferns and mosses (damp) 37
   see also ponds; seashore
Harvey, William 21
health *see* medical care
hearing 124–5, 128
   impairment 125, 126–7, **133**
   see also ear
heart ix, 20
   disease 6
heat energy (thermal energy) 84–99, **133**
   contraction 88–9, **131**
   distillation 61
   evaporation 60, 96, **132**
   expansion 88–9, **132**
   seeing *see* infrared
   stored 87
   temperature and 86–7
   thermal insulation 92–3, **138**
   transfers *see* conduction; convection; radiation
   weathering and 67
   yeast and 22
   see also boiling; melting; temperature
helium 46
   expansion with heat energy 89
   single atom 47
   speed of sound through 123
herbivore 40, 41
human body, temperature of 84
humus in soil 69, **133**
hydrogen 46, 49, 52
   in air 62

fact file 53
sulphide 55
in water 61
hydrogen peroxide 56, 59, **133**
hypothesis 22–3, **133**

ice 84
   energy stored in 87, 90
   melting 90
   weathering and 67
igneous rock 78–9, 80, 83, **133**
   see also basalt; granite
image 110, **133**
immune/immune system 27, **133**
immunised 30–1, **133**
infections 26–7, **133**
   preventing 30–1
   see also diseases
influenza 34–5
infrared camera 96, 128
infrared radiation 96, **134**
input (independent) variables 108
insulation/insulators
   sound 127, **137**
   thermal 92–3, **138**
interdependent/interdependence xi, 43, **134**
interlocking 66, **134**
intestines
   large 8, 11, **134**
   small 8, 10, 11
intuitive thinking 75
iron 52
   fact file 53
   filings 101, **134**
   magnetic 51, 100, 101, 104
   in rocks 77, 79
   speed of sound through 123
   symbol for 48
iron oxide 104

J (joules) 4, **134**
Jabir ibn-Hayyan 46
Jenner, Edward 30–1
joules (J) 4, **134**

key **134**
   variables 108, **134**
kilohertz 125, 128, **134**
kilojoules/kJ 4, **134**

large intestine 8, 11, **134**

lateral thinking 75, **134**
lava 78, **134**
lead nitrate and lead iodide 58–9
leaves 18
    cuticle 36, 37, **132**
light energy viii, 110–19, **134**
    absorbed 114
    colours 116–17, 118–19
    plants and 16
    ray 112, 113, **136**
    reflection 112–13, 117, **136**
    refraction 114–15, **136**
    scattered 112–13, **137**
    sensors 111, **134**
    source 110
    speed 111
    spotlight test 119
    see also seeing
limestone 76–7, 81, **134**
    weathering 68
line of best fit 12–13, **134**
liquids 50–1
    air 63
    heat energy and 88–9, 91
        becoming gases *see* evaporation
        becoming solids *see* freezing
        conduction 93
        convection 94–5
        gases becoming *see* condensing
        solids becoming *see* melting
    particles in ix
    sound travels through 122–3
    see also water
liver 8
lodestone 104, **134**
London, cholera in 33
loudness 121
luminous 112
lungs 18–19, 20, 26

maggots 17
magma 78, 80, **134**
magnesium 55
magnesium oxide 51, 54, **134**
magnetism/magnetic 100–9, **134**
    bar magnet 101, 102–3, **130**
    Earth's magnetic field 102–3
    electromagnets 106–9
    field 101, 102, 106, **134**
    field lines 101, 103, **134**
    making magnets 104–5

    materials 100, **134**
    metals 51, 52, 100
    permanent magnet 104–5, **135**
    temporary magnet 104, **137**
    see also compass
marble 77, 81, 83, **134**
materials 122–3, **134**
matter *see* changes of state; states of matter
medical care
    antibiotics 25, 29, **130**
    medicines 25, 29, 34–5
    operations 28
    pure oxygen 63
    see also diseases
melting 90, 91
    point 50–1, 57, 84, **134**
Mendeléev, Dmitri Ivanovich 49
meningitis 26
mercury 46, 52, 53
metals 46, 57, 77, **134**
    appearance of 50
    fact files 53
    heat energy and 98–9
        conductors 92–3
        expansion 88
        melting 50
    magnets and 51, 100
    in periodic table 48–9
metamorphic rock 80, **135**
    marble 77, 81, 83, **134**
MgO (magnesium oxide) 54, 55, **135**
microbes (microorganisms) 24–35, **135**
    defence against 26–7
    diseases and 26–7
    types of *see* bacteria; fungi; viruses
    useful 25
microphone 120, 128, **135**
minerals
    in food 3, 10, **135**
    in rocks 66, 77, 79, **135**
mirrors 113
mixtures 46, 47, 60–3, **135**
    air as 62–3
    water as 60–1
molecule 8, 47, **135**
Montague, Lady Wortley 30
Moon 112
mosses 37, **135**
moulds 24, 25
mussels 40, 41

N (newtons) x, **135**
navigating/navigate 102, **135**
negative correlation 34, 35, **135**
neutral thinking 75
Newton, Isaac 117
newtons, N x, **135**
nickel 52, 53
  magnetic 51, 100
nitrogen 62, 63
  in air 62
  condensation 63
  liquid 63
noise 126–7, **135**
non–interlocking 66, **135**
non–luminous 112
non–metals **135**
  appearance of 50
  boiling point 51
  fact files 53
  not magnetic 51
  in periodic table 48–9
non–porous 81
north pole 100, 102–3, 105, **135**
  detecting *see* compass
nucleus ix, **135**
numbers, pyramid of 40, **136**
nutrients 2, **135**
  see also food

obese 4, **135**
oil, speed of sound through 123
opaque 114, **135**
operations and antiseptics 28
organ ix, **135**
oscilloscope *see* CRO
outcome variables 108–9
oxides 55, 58, 64, 65
  see also carbon dioxide; MgO
oxygen 46, **135**
  in air 62
  appearance 50
  atoms 47
  boiling point 62
  carbon dioxide from 51
  chemical reactions and *see* oxides
  condensation point 63
  magnesium and *see* MgO
  molecule 47
  pure 63
  respiration and 14, 16
    in blood 20

breathing 18, 19
in water 38–9, 61

pancreas 8
particles/particles model ix, 47, **135**
  heat energy and 86, 88–9, 90, 93, 95, 99
Pasteur, Louis 24
pathogens 26, **135**
peas 16
penicillin 29
periodic table 48–9, 50, **135**
  groups in 48–9, **133**
  periods in 48–9, **135**
periscope 113
permanent magnet 104–5, **135**
photography 117
  see also camera
physical weathering 66–7, **136**
pinhole camera 110, **136**
pitch 120–1, 125, **136**
placebo 34, 35, **136**
plague, bubonic 32
plants
  cells ix
  counting 44–5
  flowering 36, **133**
  in food web 41
  groups 36–7
  pollination xi
  reproduction 36, 37
  respiration 16
  trees 16, 36
plastic as insulator 92–3
poles **136**
  south 100, 102, 105, **137**
  see also north pole
pollination xi
ponds 38–9, 40
  pond dipping 38–9, **136**
population 42–3, **136**
porous 66, 81, **136**
porpoise, hearing of 125
positive correlation 34, 35, **136**
precipitate 59, **136**
predation 43
prediction/predicting 22, 55, **136**
primary colour 118–19, **136**
producer xi, 40, **136**
products 58–9, **136**
properties 50, **136**
proteins 2, 8, 14, **136**

pure substances 46, 47, **136**
  melting and boiling points known 57, 62
  nitrogen 62–3
  oxygen 63
  water 60, 61
pyramid of numbers 40, **136**

quadrat 45, **136**

radiation 96–7, **136**
  infrared 96, **134**
rain and weathering 68
random sampling 45, **136**
ratio 64, **136**
rats and disease 32
ray of light 112, 113, **136**
reactants 58–9, **136**
reflecting (thinking) 75
reflection/reflects 112–13, 117, **136**
refraction/refracts 114–15, **136**
repel 101, **137**
reproduce/reproduction **137**
  by plants 36, 37
resistance, air x, **130**
respiration 14–23, **137**
  aerobic 15, **130**
  blood flow 20–1
  breathing 18–19
  maggots 17
  plants 16
  yeast 22–3
rickets **137**
rivers
  deposition by 71
  erosion by 70–1, 73
  transportation by 70–1, 72
rocks 66–83
  crystals in 66, 78, 82
  cycle 80–1, **137**
  deposition 71–3
  erosion 70–1, 73
  identifying 83
  minerals in 66, 77, 79
  molten 79
  transportation 70–1
  see also fossils; igneous; metamorphic;
    sedimentary rocks; weathering
roughage (fibre) 3, 11

salivary amylase 12
salt see sodium chloride

sampling, random 44–5, **136**
sandstone 66, 77, 80, 81, 83, **137**
scatter 112–13, **137**
scurvy 3, **137**
seal 41
seashore 39–41
  beach 39, 40
  sea shells 39, 40, 41
  seagull 41
  seawater 60
  seaweed 40, 41
secondary colours 118–19
sediment 71, **137**
  see also deposition
sedimentary layers 71, 72–3, 76, **137**
sedimentary rocks 68, 76–7, 80, 81, 83, **137**
  see also fossils; limestone; sandstone
seeds 16, 36
seeing 111, 117, 128
  heat energy 128
  see also light energy
senses 128–9
  see also hearing; seeing
sensors, light 111, **134**
sewage in drinking water 33
sexually transmitted diseases 26, **137**
shadow 110
shellfish 39, 40, 41
sight see seeing
silica 79
silver 46
skin as protection 26
small intestine 8, 10, 11
smallpox 30–1
Snow, Doctor John 33
sodium 57
sodium chloride (salt) 56–7
  formula for 64, 65
  from seawater 60
  too much in food 5, 6
sodium iodide 58
sodium nitride 65
sodium oxide 64, 65
soil 69
solids
  heat energy and 88, 90, 91
    becoming liquids see melting
    conduction 92–3
    expansion 88
    liquids becoming see freezing
  particles in ix

in periodic table 48–9, 50–1, 52
sound travels through 122–3
sound energy viii, 120–9, **137**
  insulation 127, **137**
  loudness 121
  noise 126–7, **135**
  pitch 120–1, 125, **136**
  speed of 123
  travelling 122–3
  vibration 120–1, 128, **138**
  see also hearing
source 110, **137**
south pole 100, 102, 105, **137**
space, competition for 43
spectrum 116, 117, **137**
speed
  of light 111
  of sound 123
spores 36, 37, **137**
star, light from 111
starch digested 9, 12–13
states of matter **137**
  see also changes of state; gases; liquids; solids
steel
  conducts heat 92–3
  magnetic 100, 104–5
stomach 8
storage/store viii, 87, **137**
strain energy viii, **137**
subsoil 69
sugar
  too much in food 6, 7
  yeast and 22
sulphur 46, 47, 52
  appearance of 50
  fact file 53
  hydrogen sulphide from 55
Sun
  radiation from 96
  temperature at centre 84
symbol 48, **137**

TB (tuberculosis) 26
temperature **137**
  as energy per particle 86–7
  measuring *see* Celsius
  see also heat energy
temporary magnet 104, **137**
texture 66, **137**
thermal energy **138**

conductors 92–3, **137**
insulators 92–3, **138**
see also heat energy
thermometer 84
thinking, lateral 75, **134**
tin, heating 98–9
tissue ix, **138**
tooth decay 6
topsoil 69, **138**
train, electric 107
transferred energy *see* energy transfer
translucent 114, **138**
transmitted 114, **138**
transparent 114, **138**
transport of rock particles 70–1
travelling sound 122–3
trees and forests 16, 36
Triton (moon of Neptune) 84
tuberculosis 26
tuning forks 120–1

unbalanced forces x, **138**
upthrust x, **138**

vaccination 30, **138**
vacuole ix, **138**
vacuum 93, **138**
variables 108–9
  key 108, **134**
vegetables in diet 5
veins 2, **138**
  carrying blood 20
  in plants 36, **138**
vibration 120–1, 128, **138**
  heat energy 88
villi/villus 11, **138**
viruses 24, 26, **138**
vitamins 3, 10, **138**
  C 3, **138**
volcano 78

washing powders, biological 9
water **138**
  boiling point 84
  competition for 43
  as compound 56
  contamination and cholera 33
  erosion by 70–1
  in food 3, 11
  freezing 84

heat energy and 86, 95–6
light through 114–15
magnetic needle in 105
melting ice 84
as mixture 60–1
oxygen in 38–9
in plants 36
pure 60, 61
respiration and 14, 16
in rocks 6, 67, 76
speed of sound through 123
weathering and 67, 68
wet/damp habitats 37, 38–9
yeast and 22
see also liquids
weathering 66–9, 80, **138**
chemical 68–9, **131**
physical 66–7, **136**
see also erosion
weight x, **138**
white blood cells 27, **138**
wind erosion 71
wood, speed of sound through 123

yeast 22–3, 24, 25

zinc 50, 58
oxide 58